PLANTS
OF THE THREE SISTERS REGION,
OREGON CASCADE RANGE

PLANTS
OF THE THREE SISTERS REGION,
OREGON CASCADE RANGE

by

ORLIN L. IRELAND

Bulletin No. 12

Museum of Natural History

University of Oregon

Eugene, Oregon

April 1968

PREFACE

The writer began a good many years ago collecting the plants, tramping the trails and climbing the mountains of the Sisters area with no other aim than personal enjoyment and satisfaction. The lack of any published list or manual of the plants of the region soon showed the need for such. With a little encouragement the aim was changed to include the preparation of a manual which, hopefully, would be suitable for publication that others interested might benefit. If the added aim has been fulfilled then the author will receive additional satisfaction, payment in full.

No doubt there are many plants not included, especially in the grasses and sedges, although much time and effort was spent with them. All speciments upon which this paper is based, with one or two exceptions, are in the Herbarium, Museum of Natural History, University of Oregon.

Sincere thanks and gratitude go especially to Dr. LeRoy E. Detling, Curator of the Herbarium, for the many years of assistance and encouragement and for the pleasant memories of the numerous field trips made with him. It is gratifying to have known the late Prof. L. F. Henderson, Curator 1924 to 1939, and to have benefitted by his wise counselling and assistance in the field of taxonomy. The writer is grateful to the University for the use of their facilities which provided an opportunity to an amateur botanist to better carry on the study of plants.

Orlin L. Ireland

December 1967

CONTENTS

PLANTS
OF THE THREE SISTERS REGION,
OREGON CASCADE RANGE

by

Orlin L. Ireland

INTRODUCTION

The Cascade Range extends southward from British Columbia into California. In Oregon and Washington it is breached only by the Columbia River which separates the two states. In Oregon this barrier 4000 feet or more high divides the state into sharply contrasting climatic areas. Along this high volcanic ridge occur several ice and snow covered peaks.

The Three Sisters area covered in this work is a nineteen mile segment of the Cascades lying a little north of the midpoint and includes about two hundred square miles of spectacular lava flows, forests, glaciers and snow-clad volcanic cones. From the divide the range slopes gently to the high eastern Oregon plateau, to the west it drops abruptly and is much cut by twisting steep-sided canyons. The east and west boundaries were set with the object of excluding the numerous plants common to the lower Cascades and beyond the scope of this work. The three major peaks extend above 3050 meters (10,000 feet), while Broken Top reaches 2775 m (9,100 ft). On their slopes persist seventeen glaciers mostly remnants of larger ice fields. More than one hundred lakes are scattered throughout the area. Headwaters of many streams arise on the slopes below timberline.

A considerable part of the area consists of jagged and jumbled lava flows of black to gray basalt, some perhaps no more than a few centuries old (Williams 1944). These mostly barren lava-beds support an occasional Whitebark Pine, *Penstemon* or *Cryptogramma*. Several outcroppings of obsidian occur, mostly glossy black to dull gray. On Wickiup Plain southwest of South Sister may be found chips of this rock left there by the Indians in the making of arrow-heads.

The region has been one of great volcanic activity, of successive eruptions and lava flows. With the passing of thousands of years the older basic lavas have broken and weathered to form the light sandy soil covering large areas. Here are the forests, the lakes and meadows, the sandy slopes and rocky ridges.

CLIMATE

Over most of the area the climate is severe. Freezing temperatures can occur any day of the year. The growing season is short. The area of greatest annual precipitation occurs above McKenzie Bridge and perhaps a little below the Sisters region. East of the divide it decreases sharply. Annual snowfall is heavy throughout, probably reaching above 300 inches in some parts.

Reports from stations of the U.S. Weather Bureau nearest the area show the average annual precipitation and snowfall in inches over a ten year period (U.S.D.A. 1941).

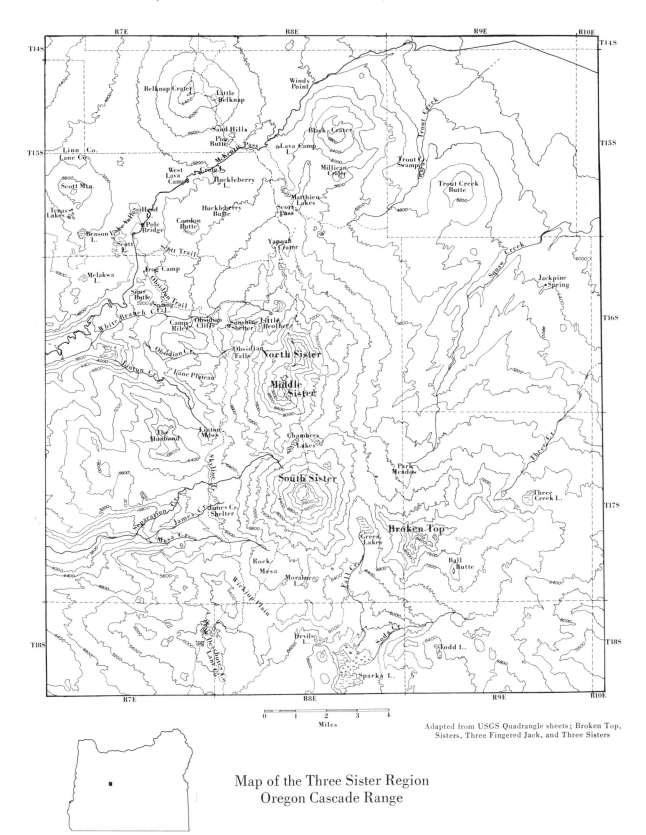

Adapted from USGS Quadrangle sheets; Broken Top,
Sisters, Three Fingered Jack, and Three Sisters

Map of the Three Sister Region
Oregon Cascade Range

North and Middle Sisters
(Photo by author)

Scott Lake
(Photo by author)

Meadow near Frog Camp
(Photo by author)

Belknap Crater
(Photo by author)

Obsidian Creek south of Sunshine Shelter
(Photo by Ray Sims)

Squaw Grass
Xerophyllum tenax
(Photo by author)

Elephant's Head
Pedicularis groenlandica var. surrecta
(Photo by author)

Marsh-Marigold
Caltha leptosepala
(Photo by author)

Sulfur Flowered Eriogonum
Eriogonum umbellatum
(Photo by author)

Western Yellow Pine
Pinus ponderosa
(Photo by author)

Lewis Monkey-Flower
Mimulus lewisii
(Photo by author)

	Precipitation	Snowfall
McKenzie Bridge, 19 miles west of the divide, elevation 425 m (1400 ft)	69.91	14.1
Sisters, 12.5 miles east, elevation 970 m (3175 ft)	16.65	57.2
Musick, 60 miles southwest, elevation about 1525 m (5000 ft)	84.76	429.2

LIFE ZONES

The system of life zones used here was developed by Dr. C. H. Merriam. The basis for these zones is the distribution of plants as determined by temperature. Areas or subdivisions result from differences caused by the moisture factor. The Merriam system as it applies to Oregon follows:

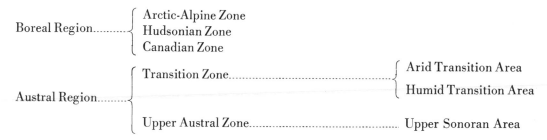

"Accompanying the altitudinal stratification of plant life, is a stratification of environmental factors" (Daubenmire 1943). In addition to temperature and precipitation are other important factors, chiefly relative humidity, soils and topography. All possible combinations of these factors can occur and when zones are adjacent considerable areas of overlapping may result. Such an area exists between the Canadian and Hudsonian Zone in the Sisters region.

The ARCTIC-ALPINE zone is the area above timberline. Thus defined it supports many plants which grow as well in the timbered sections below. A few species are confined to this zone, growing on the slopes high above the last prostrate hemlock. The largest areas are found on the Sisters and Broken Top, much smaller ones on the Husband and Ball Butte. Black Crater, 2200 meters (7200 ft) high, is entirely timbered but has a few species characteristic of this zone growing at the summit.

CHARACTERISTIC ARCTIC-ALPINE ZONE PLANTS

Cassiope mertensiana	*Oxyria digyna*
Collomia larsenii	*Phyllodoce empetriformis*
Draba aureola	*Polemonium pulcherrimum*
Hulsea nana	*Raillardella argentea*
Luetkea pectinata	*Saxifraga tolmiei*

The HUDSONIAN zone, which in its lower sections includes a variable percentage of typical Canadian Zone plants, covers a major part of the region including most of the forests and lava beds. The altitudinal range of the zone is influenced by the base level on either side of the Cascades. To the east it is about 1070 meters (3500 ft), on the western side no more than half as high. With the lower base level the zone tends to run correspondingly low. Furthermore a ridge is warmer than a draw down which the heavier cold air flows and on the warmer southwest slope the zone extends higher than on the colder northeast side (Bailey 1936).

CHARACTERISTIC HUDSONIAN ZONE PLANTS

Abies lasiocarpa	*Lupinus lepidus* var. *lyallii*
Agoseris aurantiaca	*Microseris alpestris*
Agrostis variabilis	*Mimulus lewisii*
Anemone occidentalis	*Pedicularis attolens*
Arctostaphylos nevadensis	*Penstemon davidsonii*
Aster alpigenus	*Penstemon rupicola*
Aster ledophyllus	*Pinus albicaulis*
Carex nigricans	*Polygonum newberryi*
Caltha biflora	*Rubus lasiococcus*
Caltha leptosepala	*Sorbus occidentalis*
Castilleja oreopola	*Salix commutata*
Epilobium hornemannii	*Spiraea densiflora*
Eriogonum pyrolaefolium	*Spraguea umbellata* var. *caudicifera*
var. *coryphaeum*	*Tsuga mertensiana*
Gaultheria humifusa	*Vaccinium deliciosum*
Juniperus siberica	*Veratrum viride*
Kalmia microphylla	

The CANADIAN zone occurs sparingly in the Black Crater-Trout Creek sector east of the divide mostly in areas dominated more or less by *Pinus contorta murrayana* with some *Abies grandis* and *Picea engelmannii*. This pine is found in many places in our area in the lower Hudsonian zone associated with *Abies lasiocarpa* and *Tsuga mertensiana*.

CHARACTERISTIC CANADIAN ZONE PLANTS

Abies amabilis	*Pachystima myrsinites*
Abies grandis	*Penstemon fruticosus*
Acer douglasii	*Picea engelmannii*
Alnus tenuifolia	*Pinus contorta* var. *murrayana*
Arabis holboellii var. *secunda*	*Pinus monticola*
Aster radulinus	*Pyrola secunda*
Clintonia uniflora	*Ribes lacustre*
Cornus canadensis	*Rubus parviflorus*
Gaultheria ovatifolia	*Salix scouleriana*
Linnaea borealis	*Senecio triangularis*
Lonicera conjugialis	*Sorbus sitchensis*
Lonicera involucrata	*Vaccinium membranaceum*
Mitella pentandra	*Xerophyllum tenax*

The ARID TRANSITION zone is represented by a few square miles in the northeast section, a border area of an extensive *Pinus ponderosa* forest to the east. This small territory supports a very limited number of species regularly occuring in this zone.

CHARACTERISTIC ARID TRANSITION ZONE PLANTS

Arabis divaricarpa	*Mimulus nanus*
Ceanothus velutinus	*Penstemon cinicola*
Cynoglossum occidentale	*Pinus ponderosa*
Fritillaria atropurpurea	*Prunus emarginata*
Gilia aggregata	*Purshia tridentata*
Kelloggii galioides	*Ribes petiolare*
Lupinus laxiflorus	*Stephanomeria lactucina*

Summary of the Plants of the Region

	Families	Genera	Species
Pteridophytes	5	9	10
Gymnosperms	2	6	11
Angiosperms	51	173	360
Total	58	188	380

Largest Families

	Genera	Species
Compositae	17	37
Cyperaceae	4	35
Scrophulariaceae	7	27
Graminae	12	25
Rosaceae	14	23
Ericaceae	10	21

Introduced Species

1. *Capsella bura-pastoris*
2. *Chenopodium album*
3. *Plantago major*
4. *Poa annua*
5. *Poa pratensis*
6. *Rumex acetocella*
7. *Spergularia rubra*
8. *Veronica serpyllifolia*

The map of the Three Sisters Region was prepared by Mildred R. Detling. The illustrations of representative plants of the flora were drawn by Pamela Parsons.

Abbreviations

A	Arctic-Alpine
H	Hudsonian
C	Canadian
T	Transition
AT	Arid Transition
HT	Humid Transition
US	Upper Sonoran
Ca (circa)	about
Cr	Creek
L	Lake
Mt	Mountain
Spg	Spring
Tr	Trail

Linear Measures and Approximate Equivalents

1 mm (one millimeter) = 0.1 cm = 1/25 inch

1 cm (one centimeter) = 10 mm = 0.01 m = 0.4 inch

1 m (one meter) = 100 cm = 39.4 inches

1 km (one kilometer) = 1000 m = 3,281 ft = 0.62 mile (5/8 mile)

1/25 in = 1 mm

1 in = 25 mm = 2.5 cm

1 ft = 0.3 m = 30 cm

1 mile = 5,280 ft = 1.6 km

KEY TO THE FAMILIES

BASED ON THE CHARACTERS OF PLANTS OF THE THREE SISTERS REGION

PTERIDOPHYTA   Ferns and fern-allies

Stems jointed, hollow, fluted; leaves minute,
    united around stem..1. EQUISETACEAE

Stems not as above
    Leaves grass-like, tubular, several from
        a corm-like base; sporangia borne in
        the enlarged bases of the leaves ....3. ISOETACEAE

    Leaves not as above
        Leaves small or scale-like covering
        the stem, sporangia borne in the leaf-axils or
        in terminal spikes ....2. LYCOPODIACEAE

    Leaves large, entire or dissected;
        sporangia marginal or on under surface of fronds
        Expanding leaves circinate, rhizomes scaly or hairy ....5. POLYPODIACEAE

        Expanding leaves erect, rhizomes glabrous ....4. OPHIOGLOSSACEAE

SPERMATOPHYTA   Seed Plants

Ovules and seeds not in a closed cavity,
    usually on the face of an open scale-leaf; stigmas none ....CLASS I. GYMNOSPERMAE

Ovules and seeds in a closed cavity
    surrounded by the ovary; stigma present ....CLASS II. ANGIOSPERMAE

Cotyledon one; stem with no differentiation into bark,
    wood or pith; leaves usually parallel-veined;
    floral parts most in 3's ....SUB-CLASS 1. MONOCOTYLEDONEAE

Cotyledons two; stem of bark, wood and pith;
    leaves usually net-veined; floral parts in 4's, 5's
    or 6's, never in 3's ....SUB-CLASS 2. DICOTYLEDONEAE

CLASS I. GYMNOSPERMAE

EVERGREEN TREES OR SHRUBS, MONOECIOUS, RESINOUS

Leaves long, needle-like; fruit a cone, scales imbricated; trees ....6 PINACEAE

Leaves short, stiff, sharp-pointed; fruit pulpy, berry-like; shrubs ....7. CUPRESSACEAE

Class II. Angiospermae

Sub-class Monocotyledoneae

Perianth none or rudimentary, of inconspicuous chaffy
    scales (in Potamogetonaceae staminate flowers
    with 4 sepal-like segments)
    Flowers in the axils of chaffy bracts
      Stems mostly hollow, jointed; leaves 2-ranked _____ 10. GRAMINEAE

      Stems solid; leaves 3-ranked _____ 11. CYPERACEAE

    Flowers not in the axils of chaffy bracts
      Perianth herbaceous, of 4 short-clawed sepal-like
        segments; carpels 4, separate _____ 9. POTAMOGETONACEAE

      True perianth none, of bristles or chaffy scales;
        flowers in globular heads _____ 8. SPARGANIACEAE

Perianth present, the parts glume- or petal-like
    Perianth of glume-like segments _____ 12. JUNCACEAE

    Perianth, at least in part, petal-like; carpels united
      Ovary superior _____ 13. LILIACEAE

      Ovary inferior
        Flowers regular _____ 14. IRIDACEAE

        Flowers irregular _____ 15. ORCHIDACEAE

Sub-class Dicotyledoneae

PETALS DISTINCT

A. Calyx and corolla wanting, vestigial or obscure
    Trees or shrubs; flowers unisexual, the staminate at least in aments
      Fruit a capsule; leaves alternate; seeds minute, many, comose _____ 16. SALICACEAE

      Fruit a winged nutlet or a nut; leaves simple, opposite;
        seeds not minute, not comose; ovary inferior
        Fruit a winged nutlet in a woody or thin-scaled
          cone; staminate aments drooping _____ 17. BETULACEAE

        Fruit of 1-3 nuts enclosed in a spiny involucre _____ 18. FAGACEAE

    Herbs or shrubs; flowers perfect or unisexual
      Plants parasitic, branched; fruit a 1-seeded berry _____ 20. LORANTHACEAE

      Plants not parasitic; perennial herbs; flowers in spikes;
        leaves trifoliate (*Achlys*) _____ 27. BERBERIDACEAE

A. Calyx only, or both calyx and corolla present
    B. Flowers apetalous (without petals)
      Calyx petaloid, white or colored; ovary superior:
        fruit of achenes in a head (*Anemone*) _____ 26. RANUNNCULACEAE

Calyx green or colored, small (1 cm. long or less)
   Subshrubs; stigmas 2-3; flowers perfect _____ 21. POLYGONACEAE

  Herbs, annual or perennial
    Stamens perigynous, attached to the hypanthium;
      stem leaves and stipules lacking;
      basal leaves simple, shallowly lobed _____ 31. SAXIFRAGACEAE

    Stamens hypogynous or epigynous
      Ovary inferior; leaves alternate, entire;
        fruit a 1-seeded drupe _____ 19. SANTALACEAE

      Ovary superior
        Sepals falling at anthesis _____ 26. RANUNCULACEAE

        Sepals persistent
          Fruit a solitary achene, 3-4 angled
            or lenticular; perianth colored _____ 21. POLYGONACEAE

          Fruit and urticle; seed smooth to papillate not angled;
            perianth herbaceous; leaves and calyx white mealy ___ 22. CHENOPODIACEAE

B. Flowers with calyx and corolla
  C. Corolla or calyx or both irregular
    Calyx with sepals colored, showy, as well as
      the petals and much modified in
      shape; pistils 2-5; fruit a cluster of
      follicles (*Delphinium, Aquilegia, Aconitum*) _____ 26. RANUNCULACEAE

    Calyx with sepals small and regular, if colored
      not showy; petals irregular
      Flowers papilionaceous; stamens 10 _____ 34. LEGUMINOSAE

      Flowers not papilionaceous; stamens less than 10
        Capsule 2-valved; leaves pinnately decompound;
          flowers flattened, heart-shaped _____ 28. FUMARIACEAE

        Capsule 3-valved; leaves simple, mostly entire _____ 39. VIOLACEAE

  C. Corolla regular, the petals alike or nearly so
    Ovary completely inferior, or if half-inferior
      the ovary not adnate the entire length
      of the calyx (see also *Ceanothus* spp.)
    Ovary completely inferior
      Fruit a berry or drupe
        Leaves opposite, simple, entire; fruit a drupe _____ 42. CORNACEAE

        Leaves alternate, simple, lobed; hypanthium
          produced above the ovary; fruit a
          berry; shrubs with or without prickles _____ 32. GROSSULARIACEAE

      Fruit not a berry or drupe
        Fruit a capsule, many-seeded; sepals
          and petals usually 4 _____ 40. ONAGRACEAE

Fruit splitting into 1-seeded halves at
    maturity; flowers small, in umbels;
    plant strongly odorous _____ 41. UMBELLIFERAE

Ovary half-inferior; fruit a capsule, not
    circumscissile; plant not fleshy _____ 31. SAXIFRAGACEAE

Ovary superior, free from the floral tube
  Stamens usually twice as many as the petals
    Plants aquatic; leaves floating, large, deeply cordate ____ 25. NYMPHAEACEAE

    Plants not aquatic (except *Ranunculus* spp.
      with leaves not as above)
    Sepals falling at anthesis _____ 26. RANUNCULACEAE

    Sepals not falling at anthesis
      Trees or shrubs _____ 33. ROSACEAE

      Herbs, perennial
        Sepals 2; capsule circumscissile ____ 23. PORTULACACEAE

        Sepals as many as petals or more;
          petals not lobed
          Stamens perigynous _____ 33. ROSACEAE

          Stamens hypogynous, usually united
            at base; leaves opposite _____ 38. HYPERICACEAE

  Stamens few, 5 or 10, not more than twice
    as many as the petals
  Trees or shrubs
    Fruit double samaras, long-winged; leaves
      opposite, simple, palmately-lobed _____ 36. ACERACEAE

    Fruit not a samara
      Leaves simple
        Stamens opposite the petals _____ 37. RHAMNACEAE

        Stamens alternate with the petals;
          seed with aril at base _____ 35. CELASTRACEAE

      Leaves compound; fruit a berry (*Berberis*) ____ 27. BERBERIDACEAE

  Herbs, annual or perennial
    Fruit a silique or silicle, or indehiscent;

      sepals and petals 4; stamens 6 _____ 29. CRUCIFERAE

    Fruit not as above; stamens equaling the
      petals or twice as many
      Carpels free or joined at base; fruit
        of 1-celled follicles _____ 30. CRASSULACEAE

      Carpels united; fruit a capsule
        Plant scapose; flowers solitary; staminodia
          lobed or fringed always present (*Parnassia*) ____ 31. SAXIFRAGACEAE

Plant not scapose; stamens and
    petals free from the calyx
Sepals 2, persistent; stems never with
    swollen nodes; seeds usually few_____23. PORTULACACEAE

Sepals 5; stems with swollen nodes;
    seeds usually many _____24. CARYOPHYLLACEAE

PETALS UNITED

A. Plants saprophytic, without chlorophyll; corolla
regular, petals 4, distinct _____43. ERICACEAE, subfamily MONOTROPACEAE

A. Plants with green foliage
  B. Ovary superior
    C. Corolla regular
      D. Stamens 5 or less
        Fruit a pair of slender follicles much longer than the flower; seeds
          comose: juice milky; stamens connivent above the style____47. APOCYNACEAE

        Fruit a capsule, berry or 2-4 distinct nutlets; seeds not comose;
          juice not milky
        Stamens as many as the corolla-lobes and opposite them; sterile
          stamens sometimes present; seeds many_____44. PRIMULACEAE

        Stamens alternate with corolla-lobes, of equal number or fewer;
          corolla not deeply parted
        Capsule circumscissile; corolla
          scarious; herbs_____54. PLANTAGINACEAE

        If a capsule, not circumscissile
        Fruit of 2-4 nutlets; leaves alternate_____50. BORAGINACEAE

        Fruit not of nutlets
        Anthers opening by terminal pores_____43. ERICACEAE

        Anthers opening by longitudinal slits
        Style 3-parted; ovary 3-celled; capsule opening
          by 3 valves_____48. POLEMONIACEAE

        Style, ovary and capsule not as above
        Rhizome thick, long, covered with membranous
          leaf-bases; aquatic or subaquatic _____46. MENYANTHACEAE

        Rhizome if present not thick plants of various habitats
        Stem-leaves when present ,opposite
          Capsule 1-celled; staments 4-5_____45. GENTIANACEAE

          Capsule 2-celled; staments 2 or 4_____52. SCROPHULARIACEAE

        Stem-leaves alternate; corolla 5-lobed;
          stamens 5_____49. HYDROPHYLLACEAE

    D. Staments twice as many as corolla-lobes or more; anthers
        opening by pores or tubes
        Herbs; corolla-lobes united at
          base only_____43. ERICACEAE, subfamily PYROLACEAE

        Shrubs mostly; corolla bell- or urn-shaped_____43. ERICACEAE

  C. Corolla irregular, bilabiate or spurred, the lobes quite unequal
    Plants aquatic; leaves finely dissected,
      bearing small bladders_____53. LENTIBULARIACEAE

    Plants not aquatic
      Fruit of 4 nutlets; herbage often aromatic
        and stems 4-angled_____51. LABIATAE

      Fruit a capsule, opening by valves or pores,
        several- to many-seeded_____52. SCROPHULARIACEAE

B. Ovary inferior; stamens 2-5
  Stamens free; leaves opposite
    Stipules always present (leaf-like in Galium, the
      leaves appearing whorled)_____55. RUBIACEAE

    Stipules none (except in *Sambucus* in Caprifoliaceae) fruit a berry
      or drupe (a dry 3-celled 1-seeded fruit in *Linnaea*)
      Shrubs or woody vines (*Linnaea* a creeping
        evergreen herb)_____56. CAPRIFOLIACEAE

      Herbs, perennial or annual; flowers irregular,
        the tube gibbous_____57. VALERIANACEAE

  Stamens with either filaments or anthers or both parts
      entirely or partially united; leaves alternate
      (sometimes opposite or all basal in Compositae)
    Individual flowers small, borne in a close head on
      a common receptacle, appearing as a single
      flower; surrounded by an involucre of bracts;
      flowers without sepals_____58. COMPOSITAE

    Flowers not borne in a head; sepals present; fruit
      a juicy berry; stamens opening by pores (see also *Gaultheria*, with
      fleshy calyx)_____43. ERICACEAE, subfamily VACCINIACEAE

DESCRIPTIVE FLORA

1. EQUISETACEAE   Horsetail Family
EQUISETUM L.

Equisetum arvense L. Sp. Pl. 1061. 1753. COMMON HORSETAIL. Perennial; fertile stems erect, 5-25 cm high, flesh-colored; sterile stems usually erect, 10-60 cm high, 6-14-furrowed, rough, many branches in whorls.

Infrequent in wet grassy places. H to C. West Lava Camp; Sparks L.; Trout Cr. Swamp 1355 m (4450 ft).

2. LYCOPODIACEAE   Club-moss Family

Perennial herbs, moss-like, usually trailing, stems leafy throughout; leaves small simple, in 2 or more ranks; sporangia uniform, 1-celled; spores minute, numerous.

KEY TO THE SPECIES OF LYCOPODIUM

Leaves of the ultimate aerial branches in many
rows, spreading, serrate..*L. annotinum*

Leaves of the ultimate aerial branches in
5 rows, appresed, entire..*L. sitchense*

Lycopodium annotinum L. Sp. Pl. 1103. 1753. STIFF CLUB-MOSS. Perennial, creeping stems; branches erect; leaves spreading, slightly serrate, spikes solitary.

Rare on moist banks of ponds. Lower H to C. West Lava Camp 1535 m (5036 ft).

Lycopodium sitchense Rupr. Betitr. Pflanzenk Russ. Reich. 3:30. 1845. ALASKAN CLUB-MOSS. Perennial, creeping stems; branches erect; leaves appressed, entire; spikes solitary.

Rase on moist shaded banks. H. Benson L. 1585 m (5200 ft).

3. ISOETACEAE   Quillwort Family
ISOETES L.

Small perennial grass-like plants; equatice, usually submersed; corm 2-3-lobed with branched roots and bearing a cluster of sedge-like leaves. Each leaf bears imbedded at the base one of two kinds of sporangia.

Isoetes bolanderi Engelm. Am. Nat. 8:214. 1874. BOLANDER'S QUILLWORT. Submersed; corm 2-lobed; 6-15 basal leaves 4-10 cm long, bright green, slender, tapering to point; sporangia basal, solitary in leaf axils, partly covered by vellum (membrane extending from inner surface of leaf).

Infrequent in shallow water and on muddy banks. Lower H to T. Scott L.; Craig L.; West Lava Camp.

4. OPHIOGLOSSACEAE   Adder's Tongue Family

BOTRYCHIUM Sw.

Rhizome short, bearing long fleshy roots; fronds 2 kinds; the sterile 1-4 times pinnately or ternately compound, free veined; fertile frond (sporophyl) long stalked, simple or pinnately divided, sporangia in double rows; spores abundant, yellow.

Botrychium silaifolium Presl. Rel. Haenk. 1:76 1825. LEATHERY GRAPE-FERN. Stem subterranean, very short, stout; sterile frond triangular in outline, 2 or 3 times pinnately lobed, fleshy, 7.5-15 cm long; fertile frond erect, 20-30 cm high, stout, much branched.

Rare on moist banks. H. West Lava Camp.

5. POLYPODIACEAE   Fern Family

Rhizomes long and creeping or stout and erect; fronds spreading or erect, the blades simple or 1—several times pinnatifid.

KEY TO THE GENERA OF POLYPODIACEAE

Sori marginal near tips of veins

Fronds dimorphous, the fertile blades with
contracted linear segments..*Cryptogramma*

Fronds alike

    Plants small, tufted..*Cheilanthes*

    Plants large, coarse...*Pteridium*

Sori dorsal upon the veins, separate, not marginal

    Bi-pinnate, fragile..*Cystopteris*

    Simply pinnate, coriaceous...*Polystichum*

CHEILANTHES Swartz

Cheilanthes gracillima D. C. Eaton in Torr. Bot. Mex. Bound. 234. 1859. LACE-FERN. Densely tufted, fronds 15-30 cm long; leaves 2-pinnate, the pinnules very small, crowded, tomentose beneath; stipes slender, wiry, dark brown, naked below.

Occasional, never plentiful, in rock crevices. H. Middle Sister at 2225 m (7300 ft); Windy Point 1495 m (4900 ft); Green Lakes at 2135 m (7000 ft).

CRYPTOGRAMMA R. Br.

Cryptogramma acrostichoides R. Br. in Richards. Bot. App. Frankl. Journ. 767. 1823. PARSLEY-FERN. Densely tufted, leaves dimorphous; the fertile 10-20 cm long, pinnules narrowly oblong with revolute margins; the sterile leaves 6.5-13 cm long, 3-4-pinnate, toothed.

Frequent in crevices of lava rocks. H and C. Lake Valley; Sparks L.

CYSTOPTERIS Bernh.

Cystopteris fragilis (L.) Bernh. Schrad. Neues Journ. Bot. 12:27. pl. 2, f. 9. 1806. BRITTLE-FERN. Rhizome creeping; fronds clustered, 10-25 cm high, delicate.

Occasional on moist rocky stream banks. H to AT. Sunshine Shelter 2045 m (6700 ft); Trout Cr. Swamp 1355 m (4450 ft); Soda Cr.

POLYSTICHUM Roth

Polystichum munitum Presl. Tent. Pter. 83. 1836. SWORD-FERN. Rhizome woody; fronds stiff, ascending, tufted; blades 30-60 cm long, narrow, simply pinnate, bases brown scaly.

Rare in moist open woods. H to mostly HT. Pine Butte 1645 m (5400 ft); Green Lakes at 2135 m (7000 ft).

PTERIDIUM Scop.

Pteridium aquilinum (L.) Kuhn. var. pubescens Underw. Nat. Ferns ed. 6. 91. 1900 BRACKEN WESTERN BRAKE-FERN. Rhizome woody, branching; solitary frond, to 50 cm long, pinnately decompound; pinnules entire, somewhat pubescent above, tomentose beneath; stipe stout, erect, straw-colored.

Occasional in this area at lower elevations. Lower H and C. Common on western side in HT and C. Matthieu L.; Black Crater at 1585 m (5200 ft); Scott Mt.; Sims Butte.

6. PINACEAE   Pine Family

Trees or shrubs, mostly evergreen, resinous, monoecious; leaves linear, needle-like; staminate cones with numerous stamens spirally arranged, soon deciduous; ovulate cones woody, made up of many spirally arranged scales each subtended by a bract; ovules naked, 2 at the upper side of the base of each scale; the seed with a membranous wing.

KEY TO THE GENERA OF PINACEAE

Leaves in clusters of 2-5, surrounded by sheath at base...................*Pinus*

Leaves not clustered and without sheaths

    Cones pendulous, scales persistent

       Bracts exserted (longer than the scales)...................*Pseudotsuga*

       Bracts included (shorter than the scales)

          Leaves sharp pointed, 4-angled...................*Picea*

          Leaves blunt pointed, flat...................*Tsuga*

    Cones erect, scales deciduous...*Abies*

ABIES Hill

Pyramidal evergreen trees with smooth bark becoming thick and furrowed; very resinous; branches slender, horizontal.

KEY TO THE SPECIES OF ABIES

Leaves with stomata on the silvery-white lower surface only; resin ducts near lower epidermis

   Leaves crowded and erect on branches; cones purple, oblong 8-12 cm long... *A. amabilis*

   Leaves 2-ranked, not crowded, forming flat sprays; cones greenish, cylindric, 12-18 cm long...*A. grandis*

Leaves with stomat aon both surfaces, bluish-green; resin ducts well within soft tissue; cones dark purple, oblong...................................*A. lasiocarpa*

Abies amabilis (Dougl.) Forbes, Pinetum Wob. 125 pl. 144. 1839. AMABILIS FIR. At lower altitudes this tree attains great size. In this area it grows 25-30 m (75-100 ft) high with a diameter of 50-65 cm (20-25 inches). Crown wide, dense, abruptly rounded. Branches droop. Bark smooth, thin, pale gray, near the base of old trees it is thickened and furrowed. Leaves dark green, grooved and shiny above, silvery beneath on both sides of the prominent midrib, 2-4 cm long. Cones purple, oblong, 8-12 cm long. Scales 20-25 mm wide; bracts less than half the length of the scales, tapering to a long slender tip. Seeds half as long as their shiny wings.

Infrequent in H zone, mostly C. Skyline Tr. south of McKenzie Pass 1680 m (5500 ft); West Lava Camp; Obsidian Tr. south of Frog Camp 1660 m (5450 ft).

Abies grandis Lindl. in Penny Cyclop. 1:30. 1833. GRAND FIR. Grows to a height of 45 m (150 ft), sometimes much higher; diameter 0.6-1.2 m (2-4 ft). Trunks straight, gradually tapered. Branches may extend nearly to the ground, the lower long and drooping. The upper crown a narrow open cone, rounded in age. Most of the branches characteristically sweep downward and then upward. Bark smooth gray-brown, very hard with whitish areas on younger trunks, about 2.5 cm thick. On older trees it becomes regularly marked by shallow furrows and flat ridges. Leaves yellow-green shining and grooved above, silvery white beneath, the apex notched on those of the lower crown branches, growing in two ranks forming flat sprays. Leaves slender 3-6 cm long. Cones light yellow-green, slender, oblong, 7.5-13 cm long. Scales fan-shaped 30 mm wide, bracts half as long as the scales, obcordate, irregularly toothed with short point extending from the center. Seeds light brown, half as long as the wings.

Occurs frequently on some of the lower slopes. Lower H, C and AT, most abundant in C. Trout Cr. Swamp area 1110-1355 m (3800-4450 ft); Spring L.; Sparks L.

Abies lasiocarpa (Hook.) Nutt. N. Am. Sylva 3:38. 1849. ALPINE FIR. Grows 18-28 m (60-90 ft) high with a diameter of 35-60 cm (14-24 inches). Crown very long, narrowly conical, extending to the ground. Branches stout, dense. Bark thin, hard, light gray with numerous large resin blisters. Leaves blue-green, silvery when new; apex rounded on those of the lower crown branches. Characteristically the dense leaves are crowded on the upper sides of the branches. Lower branch leaves 1.5-3.5 cm long, those of the upper branches shorter. Mature cones 6-9 cm long, dark purple. Scales 25 mm long and as broad. Bract less than half as long as the scales, cut margins, abruptly tipped.

Common throughout H zone. McKenzie Pass; Frog Camp; Sparks L.; Three Creek L.; Green Lakes.

PICEA Link

Tall pyramidal evergreen trees with thin scaly bark; leaves spirally arranged on the branches and extending outward from all sides, stiff, pointed; cone scales thin, flexible, persistent.

Picea engelmannii (Parry) Engelm. Trans. St. Louis Acad. 2:212. 1863. ENGELMAN'S SPRUCE. In this area it grows mostly in open stands reaching a height of 25 m (80 ft), a diameter of 60 cm (2 ft). Crown narrowly pyramidal, lower branches drooping, often extending to the ground. Bark scaly, brownish-gray. Leaves about 25 mm long, 4-angled, flexible, sharp-tipped. Cones pendent, 5-6.5 cm long, light brown shiny; scales thin, flexible, crinkled, persistent. Seeds blackish, wing broad.

Occasional, always few in number in moist places. Lower H and C both sides of divide. West Lava Camp; Scott L.; Spring L.; Three Cr. L.; Trout Cr. Swamp area.

PINUS L.

Evergreen trees with scaly or furrowed bark, leaves in clusters of 2-5.

KEY TO THE SPECIES OF PINUS

Leaves 5 in cluster (fascicle)

    Cones ovoid, scales very thick; seed longer than wing.................................*P. albicaulis*

    Cones cylindric, scales thin; seed much shorter than wing........................*P. monticola*

Leaves 2 or 3 in cluster

    Clusters 2-leaved, ca 5 cm long, cones small..*P. contorta*

    Clusters 3-leaved, 15-20 cm long, cones large (7-10 cm) ....*P. ponderosa*

A *Lycopodium annotinum;* **B** *Isoetes bolanderi;* **C,D** *Cryptogramma acrostichoides;*
E *Pinus albicaulis;* **F** *Tsuga mertensiana*

Pinus albicaulis Engelm. Trans. St. Louis Acad. 2:209. 1863. WHITE-BARK PINE. Low usually twisted trunk 5-15 m (15-50 ft) high; branches stout and flexible forming broad irregular crown. At timberline it grown prostrate with many large spreading branches. Leaves 5 in cluster 3-5 cm long, rather stout, usually slightly curved. Bark thin, mostly smooth, whitish to brown. Cones oval 5-8 cm long, purplish; scales thick, not spreading at maturity. Seeds 12 mm long, dark brown, hard; wings narrow, remaining attached to the scales.

Scattered throughout H zone. McKenzie Pass area; Black Crater 1500-2200 m (4900-7200 ft); Scott Mt.; Wickiup Plain; Green Lakes and all the higher peaks to timberline.

Pinus contorta Loud. var. **murrayana** (Balf.) Engelm. in S. Wats. Bot. Calif. 2:126. 1880. LODGE-POLE PINE. Variable, in dense stands it grows 12 to 25 m (40-80 ft) high with clean slender trunks 20-45 cm (8-18 in) in diameter. Crowns short and narrow. In open stands the crown is dense, usually rounded; the branches larger, often extending to the ground. Bark very thin, about 6 mm, light brownish-gray, scaly. Leaves 2 in cluster, yellow-green. Cones ovoid, oblique, 25-38 cm long. Scale tips of mature cones shiny chestnut brown armed with slender prickles, the inner parts purplish-brown. Seeds deep reddish-brown with darker spots, 4 mm long with wings 2 or 3 times as long.

Widely scattered in the H zone with *Abies lasiocarpa* and *Tsuga mertensiana*; often dominating in Lake Valley and Sparks L. areas. At Green Lakes and Black Crater it extends to near timberline. Near Trout Cr. Butte are occasional dense stands in the C zone.

Pinus monticola Dougl. Lamb. Pinus ed. 2, 3:27. pl. 67. 1837. WESTERN WHITE PINE. In this area usually small, to 25 m (80 ft) high; diameter to 75 cm (30 in). Leaves 5 in a cluster, slender, glaucous, straight, 5-10 cm long. Bark of mature trees 2-3.5 cm thick, shallow furrows forming small square plates, grayish-purple in dense stands to brown when growing more widely spaced. Bark of young trees smooth, gray. Cones slender 15-23 cm long, ends of scales light brown, inner parts dark reddish-brown. Seeds 9 cm long, brown spotted with black; wings 22 mm long, acute.

Few and scattered in Lake Valley and Sparks L. areas. Lower H to mostly C. Pine Butte; Sims Butte; Black Crater.

Pinus ponderosa Dougl. Lawson, Agric. Man. 354. 1836. PONDEROSA PINE. WESTERN YELLOW PINE. In its upper range it seldom exceeds 12 m (40 ft) in height. Lower in the Trout Cr. Butte area it may reach 43 m (140 ft) or more with a diameter of 90-120 cm (3-4 ft). Trunk long smooth and straight; crown open. Leaves 3 in a cluster, 12-24 cm long. Bark 5-8 cm thick, fissured, forming broad russet-red plates, the surface made up of small well formed scales. On smaller trees the bark is blackish-brown, narrowly furrowed. Cones ovoid 7-10 cm long; ends of scales russet-brown, shiny with a short prickle. Seeds dull yellowish with dark purple blotches, wings broadest below middle.

Rare in lower H zone in McKenzie Pass-Black Crater section. In the Trout Cr. Butte-Cow Camp area the extensive stands of the AT zone to the east give way largely to *Abies grandis, Picea engelmannii* and *Pinus contorta marrayana*. Pine Butte; West Lava Camp; Matthieu L.; Park Meadow 1860 m (6100 ft).

PSEUDOTSUGA Carr.

Tall pyramidal evergreen trees with thick furrowed bark, branches in whorls; leaves appearing 2-ranked.

Pseudotsuga menziesii (Mirbel) Franco, Bio. Soc. Brot. 24:74. 1950. DOUGLAS FIR. (*P. taxifolia* Brill.). In the Trout Cr. area east of the divide it grows to a height of 25-30 m (80-100 ft) having a diameter of 45-75 cm (18-30 in). Crown pyramidal, may become rounded. Bark very thick, outer dark brown, inner red-brown; rough with large ridges and deep furrows. Leaves dark yellow-green to blue-green 20-30 mm long. Cones 5-8 cm long, elliptic, pendent; bracts much exceeding the scales. Seeds dull russet-brown with lighter blotches, wings about twice as long.

Enters the area in the northeastern section only. West of the Cascade Range mainly in the HT zone it is by far the most common coniferous tree and the largest. Heights of 45-70 m (150-230 ft) are not uncommon. They are the source of vast amounts of lumber cut each year.

TSUGA Carr.

Pyramidal evergreen trees with slender horizontal branches.

Tsuga mertensiana (Bong.) Sarg. Sylva N. Am. 12:77. 1898. MOUNTAIN HEMLOCK. Grows up to 25 m (80 ft) high with a diameter of 65 cm (25 in). Narrow, pointed, pyramidal crown; slender drooping branches extending to the ground. Bark hard, rough, scaly, deeply divided into narrow ridges, dark reddish-brown, 30 mm thick. Leaves 1-1.5 cm long, obtuse, plump, spreading from all sides of the branchlets. Cones abundant, usually pendulous, cylindric, narrowed at both ends, about 45 mm long. Color of mature cones variable, light brown after opening. Scales thin, broad; bracts ¼ as long.

Occurs throughout H zone, often dominant especially on north slopes. Forming prostrate mats it is the last tree at timberline. Middle Sister at 2290 m (7500 ft); Lake Valley; Green Lakes; Black Crater, dominant at 1770 m (5800 ft).

7. CUPRESSACEAE   Cypress Family

Trees or shrubs with short, pointed leaves in whorls of 3, or scale-like, opposite.

JUNIPERUS L.

Juniperus communis L. var. **montana** Ait. Hort. Kew 3:414. 1788. DWARF JUNIPER. Low spreading shrub; thin sheddy bark; leaves in close whorls of 3, linear, sharp pointed with broad white longitudinal band above, convex and green below. Berries globose, 5-8 mm broad, blue with bloom.

Occasional in open woods and above timberline. H and A. McKenzie Pass area; Lake Valley; Middle Sister at 2230 m (7300 ft).

8. SPARGANIACEAE   Bur-reed Family

One genus only, aquatic herbacious perennials; creeping rhizomes, fibrous roots; stems erect or floating; leaves linear, alternate, 2-ranked, parallel-veined; flowers monoecious in globose heads, the staminate above; stamens 3-6; pistillate flowers subtended by a few linear scales.

SPARGANIUM L.

Sparganium angustifolium Michx. Fl. Bor. Am. 2:189. 1803. NARROW-LEAVED BUR-REED. Stems slender, floating, 30-50 cm high; leaves long, narrow, 2-6 mm wide; fruiting heads bur-like, few, 10-15 mm in diameter; achenes stipitate, long beaked.

Occasional in shallow water, borders of lakes. H to T. Scott L.; Tenas Lakes; Matthieu L. 1785 m (5850 ft).

9. POTAMOGETONACEAE   Pondweed Family

POTAMOGETON L.

Perennial aquatic herbs, stems submerged; leaves 2-ranked, stipulate and more or less sheathing, submerged or floating or both. Submerged leaves usually linear, the floating broader; flowers perfect in sessile or peduncled spikes; stamens 4; pistils 4, sessile, 1-celled; fruit of 4 druplets.

KEY TO THE SPECIES OF POTAMOGETON

Submerged leaves linear to lanceolate; floating leaves
  ovate to elliptic-oblong, or wanting..*P. heterophyllus*

Submerged leaves filiform, without blades; floating leaves
  broadly oval or elliptic with rounded or subcordate base.............................*P. natans*

Potamogeton heterophyllus Schreb. Spicil. Fl. Lips. 21. 1771. VARIOUS-LEAVED PONDWEED. Submerged leaves thin, 7.5-15 cm long, 0.5-1 cm wide; spikes cylindric 1-2 cm long.

Rare in ponds and lakes. H. to T. Todd L. 1860 m (6100 ft).

Potamogeton natans L. Sp. Pl. 126. 1753. COMMON FLOATING PONDWEED. Stems mostly simple.. Floating leaves 4-7 cm long on petioles up to 3 times as long; submerged leaves without blades and usually not lasting; spikes about 4 cm long.

Rare in ponds and lakes. H to T. Sparks L. 1645 m (5400 ft).

10. GRAMINEAE (POACEAE)   Grass Family

Annual or perennial herbs; stems (culms) hollow, closed at the nodes; the alternate, 2-ranked, paralled-veined leaves consist of the usually linear, flat blade and the sheath at the base which envelops the culm and bears on the inside a hyaline or hairy appendage, the ligule.

Flowers mostly perfect, small, with no distinct perianth, arranged in spikelets consisting of a shortened axis (rachilla) and 2 to many 2-ranked bracts, the lowest 2 being empty (the glumes, rarely one or both obsolete), the one or more succeeding ones (lemmas) bearing in their axils a single flower, and between the flower and the rachilla a second 2-nerved bract (the palea), the lemma, palea, and flower together constituting the floret; stamens 1 to 6, usually 3, with very delicate filaments and 2-celled anthers; pistil 1, with a 1-celled 1-ovuled ovary, 2 (rarely 1 or 3) styles, and usually plumose stigmas; fruit a caryopsis (grain, the single seed and fruit being united).

The spikelets are usually aggregated in spikes or panicles at the ends of the main culms or branches. The parts of the spikelet may be modified in various ways. The first glume or more rarely also the second may be wanting. The lemmas may contain no flower, or even no palea, or may be reduced, or rudimentary.

KEY TO THE TRIBES

Spikelets sessile on the rachis, the rachis disarticulating
    in *Hordeum* and *Sitanion*..4. HORDEAE
Spikelets pedicellate in open or contracted
    (sometimes spike-like) panicles
  Spikelets 1-flowered..1. AGROSTIDEAE
  Spikelets 2-many-flowered
    Glumes as long as the lowest floret, usually as long as the
      spikelet; lemmas awned from the back (awnless in *Koeleria*)............2. AVENEAE
    Glumes shorter than the first floret, lemmas awnless
      or awned from the tip..3. FESTUCEAE

Tribe 1. AGROSTIDEAE

Fruit indurate, terete, awned, nerves obscure; callus usually well
        developed, oblique, usually acute, bearded; awn
        persistent, twisted, bent ,several to many times longer
        than the slender fruit..*Stipa*
Fruit thin or firm, not indurate, if firm the nerves prominent or
      evident, callus not well developed
  Glumes longer than the lemma (equaling it only in *Agrostis
      thurberiana* and *A. aequivalvis*)
    Glumes compressed-carinate, abruptly mucronate, stiffly
      ciliate on the keels; panicle dense..*Phleum*
    Glumes not compressed-carinate, not ciliate on
      the keels; panicle open or contracted
      Florets with hairs at base half as long as the
        lemma; palea present..*Calamagrostis*
      Florets naked at base or with short hairs................................*Agrostis*
  Glumes not longer than the lemma, usually shorter; lemma
    awned from the tip or mucronate; 3-5 nerved................................*Muhlenbergia*

AGROSTIS L. Bentgrass

Palea evident, 2-nerved, more than half as long as the lemma
  Rachilla prolonged behind the palea as a minute bristle; lemma
      glabrous, awnless; spikelets 2 mm long, purple................................*A. thurberiana*
  Rachilla not prolonged; glumes scabrous on the keel only;
      panicle somewhat open; no long stolons; culms
      decumbent at base; no rhizomes..*A. stolonifera*
Palea obsolete, 0.5 mm or less in length, plants without rhizomes
  Panicle narrow, contracted, at least some of the lower
      branches spikelet-bearing from near the base
    Culms slender, in dense tufts; basal leaves numerous;
      blades 3-5 cm long, 1 mm wide; panicle about 5 mm wide................*A. variabilis*
    Culms stouter, not in tufts with dense basal leaves; blades
      longer and wider; panicle rather dense to open; plants
      much taller; palea less than one-fourth as long as the lemma................*A. exarata*
  Panicle open; lower branches not spikelet-bearing at the
    base; many of the lemmas with awns, attached at the
    middle or above..*A. scabra* var.

Agrostis exarata Trin. Gram. Unifl. 207. 1824. WESTERN BENT-GRASS. Culms 25-75 cm high, somewhat tufted; sheaths mostly smooth, ligules 4 mm long or more; blades flat, 2-6 mm wide, scabrous; panicle narrow, somewhat open to dense and interrupted, 5-20 cm long; glumes subequal, acuminate, 2-3 mm long, scabrous on the keel and occasionally sparsely so on the margins and back; lemma 1.5-2 mm long, not awned; palea minute.

Infrequent in meadows. H. Linton Cr. near Skyline Tr. at 2045 m (6700 ft).

Agrostis scabra Willd. var. **geminata** (Trin.) Swallen, Wash. Biol. Soc. Proc. 54. 1941. TICKLEGRASS. Culms tufted, slender, 15-25 cm high; leaves mostly basal, very narrow; branches of the panicle little spreading, long, slender, scabrous, bearing the spikelets near the ends; glumes about 2 mm long, unequal, acuminate, scabrous on the keels; lemma 1.5-1.7 mm long, with or without awn, callus sparsely pilose.

Occasional in mountain meadows. H. West Lava Camp; Hand L.

Agrostis stolonifera L. Sp. Pl. 62. 1753. SPREADING BENTGRASS. Culms. erect, 25-50 cm high, spreading by rooting of the decumbent lower parts; ligules 2-5 mm long, scabrous; blades flat, 5-15 cm long, 2-5 mm wide; panicle oblong, 10-15 cm long, usually purple, somewhat open, most branches spikelet-bearing from near the base; glumes 2-2.5 mm long, acute, glabrous except scabrous on the keel; lemma shorter than the glumes, obtuse, not awned; palea half as long as the lemma or slightly longer.

Infrequent in meadows. Probably not native in Oregon. Lower H. Craig L.; Pole Bridge 1465 m (4800 ft).

Agrostis thurberiana Hitchc. U. S. Dept. Agr. Bur. Pl. Ind. Bul. 68:25 pl. 1. f. 1. 1905. THURBER's BENTGRASS. Culms 20-40 cm high, tufted, slender; leaves 2 mm wide or less, mostly basal; panicle narrow, lax; spikelets green, pale or purple, 2 mm long; lemma nearly as long as the glumes, palea two-thirds as long.

Occasional in moist places. H. West Lava Camp; Pole Bridge; Linton Meadows 1860 m (6100 ft).

Agrostis variabilis Rydb. Mem. N. Y. Bot. Gard. 1:32. 1900. (*A. rossae* Vasey, Contrib. U. S. Natl. Herb. 3:76. 1892) ROSS BENTGRASS or REDTOP. Culms 10-20 cm high, densely tufted; blades mostly 1 mm wide or less; panicle contracted, branches appressed, 2-6 mm long; spikelets 2 mm long, purple or green;

lemma 1.5 mm long, awnless; palea minute.

Common in open places. A and H. McKenzie Pass; Scott Mt.; White Branch Cr.; Wickiup Plain; Todd L.; Green Lakes 2000 m (6550 ft).

CALAMAGROSTIS Adans. Reedgrass

Calamagrostis canadensis (Michx.) Beauv. Ess. Agrost. 15. 157. 1812. BLUE-JOINT. Culms 60 or more cm high, tufted; rhizomes creeping; blades 4-8 mm wide, flat, scabrous, lax; panicle narrow to open; glumes 3-4 mm long, scabrous on the keel, acuminate; lemma usually little shorter than the glumes, glabrous; awn mostly straight, attached below the middle, extending to the tip; callus hairs abundant, about equaling the lemma.

Frequent in moist meadows and open woods. H. West Lava Camp; McKenzie Pass; Fall Cr. near Sparks L. 1680 m 5500 ft).

MUHLENBERGIA Schreb. Muhly

Muhlenbergia filiformis (Thurb.) Rydb. Bull. Torrey Club 32:600. 1905. SLENDER MUHLY. Perennial, sometimes appearing annual; culms clustered, erect or decumbent at base, very slender, 15 or more cm high; blades flat, very short; panicle short, narrow, interrupted, few-flowered; glumes 1 mm long, ovate; lemma acute, 2 mm long.

Infrequent in open woods and meadows. H. McKenzie Pass; Scott L.

PHLEUM L. Timothy

Phleum alpinum L., Sp. Pl. 59. 1753. MOUNTAIN TIMOTHY. Culms 20-50 cm high, mostly glabrous; blades 10 cm long or less, 4-6 mm wide; panicle narrow, dense, spike-like, short-cylindric, bristly; glumes about 5 mm long, with awn 2 mm long.

Frequent in moist meadows. A and H. Scott L.; Three Creek L.; Todd L.

STIPA L. Needlegrass

Stipa occidentalis Thurb.; S. Wats., in King, Geol. Expl. 40th Par. 5:380. 1871. WESTERN STIPA. Culms 30-60 cm high, tufted, slender; blades narrow, involute; sheaths glabrous mostly, ligule 1 mm long; panicle narrow; glumes 8 or more mm long, acuminate, glabrous; lemma 6 mm long, pilose, the awn 2.5 or more cm long, twice-geniculate, pilose to the second bend or to the tip.

Frequent in dry open woods. H to AT. McKenzie Pass; Sunshine Shelter 2045 m (6700 ft).

Tribe 2. AVENEAE

Lemmas convex, awned from below the middle..*Deschampsia*

Lemmas keeled, bidentate, awned from above the middle.................................*Trisetum*

DESCHAMPSIA Beauv. Hairgrass

Glumes exceeding florets; blades thin, flat...*D. atropurpurea*

Glumes not exceeding the upper floret; blades firm......................................*D. caespitosa*

Deschampsia atropurpurea (Wahl.) Scheele, Flora 27:56. 1844. MOUNTAIN HAIRGRASS. Perennial; culms 40-60 cm high, loosely tufted, purplish at base; blades soft, ascending, apex acute, 3-5 mm wide; panicle open, the few branches slender, drooping, naked below; glumes about 5 mm long, purplish; lemmas about 2 mm long, the awn of the first straight, included, of the second, geniculate, exserted.

Occasional in moist meadows and open woods. H. White Branch Cr.; Obsidian Cliffs 1890 m (6200 ft): Green Lakes.

Deschampsia caespitosa Beauv. Ess. Agrost. 91, 160. pl. 18. f. 3. 1812. TUFTED HAIRGRASS. Perennial; culum densely tufted, 60-100 cm high, leafy at base; sheaths smooth: blades mostly folded, scabrous above: ligules 5 mm long or more: panicle open, drooping, the branches slender, scabrous, bearing spikelets toward the ends: spikelets about 4 mm long; florets distant: glumes narrow, acute, about as long as the florets: lemmas smooth: callus hairs dense, short: awn from near the base, longer than the lemma, straight to slightly bent.

Common in moist meadows and open woods. H to T. Hand L.; Green Lakes; Linton Meadows.

TRISETUM Pers.

Trisetum spicatum (L.) Richt. Pl. Eur. 1:59. 1890. DOWNY OATGRASS. Culms 20-50 cm high, erect, densely tufted, puberulent below the panicle; blades and sheaths puberulent or glabrous; panicle spike-like, compact, some interrupted below, 6-12 cm long, mostly pale green or purplish; spikelets 5-8 mm long, glumes unequal in length, glabrous, the keels scabrous; lemmas scaberulous; awns attached one-third below the tip, about 6 mm long, geniculate, exserted.

Frequent on dry open slopes. A and upper H. Scott Mt.: Obsidian Cliffs; Mesa Cr. at about 1800 m (5900 ft): Broken Top above 2440 m (8000 ft); Ball Butte at 2440 m (8000 ft).

Tribe 3. FESTUCEAE

Nerves of the lemma parallel, not converging at summit or but
    slightly so: nerves prominent...*Glyceria*

Nerves of the lemma converging toward summit, lemmas narrowed
    at apex, entire, pointed, awnless or awned from tip
    Spikelets awned; lemmas pointed...*Festuca*

    Spikelets awnless, on slender pedicels in compound panicles....................*Poa*

FESTUCA L. Fescue

Lemmas 7-10 mm long, scabrous, rarely short-awned; culms scabrous............*F. scabrella*

Lemmas not more than 7 mm long; culms smooth
    Lemmas awnless...*F. viridula*

    Lemmas awned
        Awn 6-7 mm long, as long as or longer than body of lemma..............*F. occidentalis*

        Awn 2-4 mm long, shorter than body of lemma........................*F. idahoensis*

Festuca idahoensis Elmer, Bot. Gaz. 36:53. 1903. IDAHO BUNCHGRASS. Culms densely tufted, 30-100 cm high; leaves mostly basal, involute, filiform, firm, scabrous, 15-30 cm long or longer; panicle 10 cm long or longer, the slender scabrous branches ascending; spikelets 5-7 flowered, not numerous; glumes acute, the first half as long as the second; lemmas about 7 mm long, nearly terete; awn 2-4 mm long.

Observed only in NE section. Common in AT. Trout Cr. road 1160 m (3800 ft).

Festuca occidentalis Hook Fl. Bor. Am. 2:249. 1840. WESTERN FESCUE. Culms 40-80 cm high, densely tufted, slender; blades mostly basal, involute, filiform, smooth; sheaths smooth; panicle narrow, few branches; spikelets 3-5 flowered, on slender pedicels; glumes glabrous, the lower shorter than the upper; lemmas 5-7 mm long, thin, scaberulous above, tipped with a slender awn as long or longer.

Rare in dry open ground. Lower H to mostly T. McKenzie Pass.

Festuca scabrella Torr. Hook. Fl. Bor. Am. 2:252. 1840. BUFFALO BUNCHGRASS or ROUGH FESCUE. Culms 30-90 cm high, densely tufted; blades 10-30 cm long, firm, involute, pointed, scaberulous; lower sheaths smooth; ligule short; panicle 5-15 cm long, narrow, branches ascending, mostly in pairs, bearing spikelets above the middle; spikelets 8-12 mm long, 3-5-flowered; glumes unequal, nearly glabrous; lemmas 6-8 mm long, scaberulous, tipped with a short awn.

Infrequent in dry woods. H to mostly AT. Wickiup Plain.

Festuca viridula Vasey, U.S. Dept. of Agr. Div. Bot. Bull. 13²:pl. 93. 1893. MOUNTAIN BUNCHGRASS. Culms 50-100 cm high, tufted, smooth; blades 1-2 mm wide, flat or involute, scabrous above, smooth beneath; sheaths smooth; panicle loose, open, 7-15 cm long; spikelets 9-12 mm long, 3-6-flowered; glumes 4-6 mm long; lemmas 6-7 mm long, firm, keeled toward apex, acute or slightly mucronate.

Frequent in meadows and open woods. H. Lake Valley; White Branch Cr.; Sunshine Shelter; east of Ball Butte.

GLYCERIA R. Br. Mannagrass

Glyceria pauciflora Presl. Rel. Haenk. 1:257. 1830. FEW-FLOWERED MANNAGRASS. Culms 40-120 cm high from creeping rhizomes; blades scabrous, acute, 10-20 cm long, 4-12 mm wide; sheaths mostly scabrous; panicle 10-20 cm long, green or purplish, branches slender, 2 or more at a node, spreading, spikelet-bearing above the middle; spikelets 4-6 mm long, ovate or oblong, 4-6-flowered; glumes obtuse, short, 1-1.5 mm long; lemmas about 2 mm long, prominently 5-nerved, scabrous, more so on the nerves, the tip scarious, erose.

Infrequent in swamps and wet meadows. AT and C. Trout Cr. Swamp 1335 m (4450 ft).

POA L. Bluegrass

Plants annual; lemmas villous on the nerves below ....*P. annua*

Plants perennial
    Creeping rhizomes present; lemmas 3 mm long,
        with a tuft of cobwebby hairs at base ....*P. pratensis*

    Creeping rhizomes wanting; not with a tuft
        of cobwebby hairs at base of lemma
    Lemmas villous on the nerves ....*P. stenantha*

    Lemmas not villous on the nerves,
        sometimes pubescent on lower part of back
    Lemmas minutely pubescent on lower half or third,
        the hairs somewhat curled, plant stout ....*P. canbyi*

    Lemmas glabrous or scabrous,
        panicle short, compact or open,
        less than 10 cm long; alpine grasses
    Blades of the culm flat, those of the lower culm
        2-3 mm wide; panicle compact, spike-like,
        long exserted, mostly purple ....*P. epilis*

    Blades narrow or filiform, usually folded or involute,
        short, rather firm; panicle narrow,
        branches short and appressed ....*P. pringlei*

Poa annua L. Sp. Pl. 68. 1753. ANNUAL BLUEGRASS. Culms tufted, 5-30 cm high, compressed; blades short, soft, lax, glabrous; panicle pyramidal, 3-6 cm long; spikelets 4-5 mm long, somewhat crowded, 3-6-flowered, purplish; lemma pilose on lower half, not webbed at base.

Introduced from Europe. Rare in area. Trout Cr. Swamp.

Poa canbyi (Scribn.) Piper, Contr. U. S. Nat. Herb. 11:132. 1906. CANBY BLUEGRASS. Culms tufted, 50-120 cm high, smooth; blades 1-2 mm wide, usually flat, scabrous above; sheaths mostly smooth; ligule 2-5 mm long; panicle 10-15 cm long, narrow, mostly compact, branches short, appressed; spikelets 3-5-flowered; lemmas pubescent on lower part of back.

Infrequent, east of divide in dry sandy soil. H to AT. Green Lakes.

Poa epilis Scribn., U. S. Dept. Agr. Div. Agrost. Cir. 9:5. 1899. MOUNTAIN BLUEGRASS. Culms 20-40 cm high, smooth, mostly solitary; blades smooth, 2-3 mm wide; sheaths glabrous; ligules about 3 mm long; panicle dense, spike-like, 2-6 cm long, purplish; spikelets 3 or more flowered; glumes about 4 mm long; lemmas 4-6 mm long, mostly glabrous.

Occasional in open woods and meadows. H and A. Camp Agoseris 1890 m (6200 ft); Green Lakes Trail at 1830 m (6000 ft).

Poa pratensis L., Sp. Pl. 67. 1753. KENTUCKY BLUEGRASS. Perennial, from creeping rhizomes; culms tufted, 20-100 cm high; blades 2-5 mm wide, glabrous, mostly flat; sheaths smooth; ligules 2 mm long; panicle open, pyramidal, the branches slender, spreading, naked at base; spikelets 3-5-flowered; lemmas copiously webbed at base, pilose on the keel and margins, 3 mm long.

Introduced from Europe, an escape from cultivation. Wide-spread, but rare in the area. Trout Cr. Swamp.

Poa pringlei Scribn., Bull. Torrey Club 10:31. 1883. PRINGLE'S BLUEGRASS. Culms tufted, 10-20 cm high; blades short, mostly basal, smooth, folded or involute; sheaths smooth, loose, becoming papery; ligules about 2 mm long; panicle narrow, somewhat condensed; spikelets purplish, 3-5-flowered; glumes equal, 3-5 mm long, glabrous; lemmas 5-6 mm long, smooth or slightly scabrous.

Frequent on high rocky slopes. A. Occurs in timberline areas on all the major peaks.

Sparganium angustifolium

Poa stenantha Trin. Mem. Acad. St. Petersb. VI. Math. Sci. Nat. 1:376. 1831. NARROW-FLOWERED BLUEGRASS. Culms tufted, 20-40 cm high; leaves mostly basal, the blades 1-3 mm wide, flat to loosely folded; ligules 2 mm long or less; sheaths smooth; panicle 5-10 cm long, rather open, the branches slender, mostly 2's; spikelets to 8 mm long, 4-6-flowered, purplish; glumes about 4 mm long; lemmas about 6 mm long, keel scabrous, pubescent toward sparsely webbed base; callus smooth.

Occasional in mountain meadows. H and above timberline. Middle Sister at 2320 m (7600 ft); Sunshine Shelter; Obsidian Cliffs; Green Lakes 2000 m (6550 ft).

Tribe 4. HORDEAE

Spikelets 3 at each node of the rachis,
1-flowered, lateral pair pediceled ....*Hordeum*

Spikelets 2 at each node of the rachis,
alike, 2-6 flowered ....*Sitanion*

HORDEUM L. Barley

Hordeum nodosum L. Sp. Pl. ed. 2. 1:126. 1762. MEADOW BARLEY. Perennial, tufted; culms 25-60 cm high; blades 4-6 mm wide, scabrous; sheaths mostly glabrous; spikes 5-8 cm long, slender; glumes setaceous, about 15 mm long; lateral spikelets small, short-awned; middle spikelet with awn longer than the glumes.

Infrequent in meadows. H to T. Soda Cr. at 1545 m (5600 ft).

SITANION Raf. Squirreltail

Sitanion hystrix (Nutt.) J. G. Smith, U. S. Dept. Agr. Div. Agrost. Bull. 18:15 pl. 2. 1899. BOTTLEBRUSH SQUIRRELTAIL. Culms tufted, 20-50 cm high; blades 6-10 cm long, 2-4 mm wide, flat to involute, mostly glabrous below, scabrous above; sheaths glabrous to pubescent; spike 2-8 cm long (the long awns excluded), exserted; glumes narrow, 1-2-nerved, the nerves extending into long, scabrous awns; lemmas mostly scabrous, the awns of glumes and lemmas spreading, 4-6 cm long; rachis readily breaking when mature.

Common dry sandy soil. A to AT. Scott Mt.; Obsidian Cliffs; South Sister; Three Creek L.

11. CYPERACEAE Sedge Family

Annual or perennial grass-like or rush-like plants, some with long horizontal rhizomes; roots fibrous; stems sometimes hollow. terete or 3- or 4-sided; leaves narrow, many with closed sheaths, 3-ranked; flowers perfect, monoecious or dioecious, in spikes or spikelets; perianth wanting or of bristles or scales; stamens mostly 3; ovary 1-celled, ovule one; styles 2-3-cleft; achenes lenticular or triangular.

KEY TO THE GENERA OF CYPERACEAE

Flowers all imperfect, mostly monoecious, rarely dioecious;
ovary enclosed in a perigynium...*Carex*

Flowers mostly perfect, spikelets terminal and solitary
with scales spirally overlapping
Style base persistent, forming a tubercle on the achene.................................*Eleocharis*

Style base not persistent on the achene
Perianth bristles many, soft, much elongated.................................*Eriophorum*

Perianth bristles few, short...*Scirpus*

CAREX L.

Perennial from rootstocks; leaves grass-like, 3-ranked; stems mostly 3-angled, phyllopodic; plants monoecious, sometimes dioecious. Spikes one to many, the flowers subtended by small scales, perianth wanting. Staminate flowers with 3 stamens, filaments filiform; pistillate flowers with 1 carpel, 1 ovule, style with 2-3 stigmas. Ovary completely enclosed in the sac-like perigynium; achene 3-sided, biconvex or plano-convex.

KEY TO THE SECTIONS

Spike 1, stigmas 3, achenes triangular
    Perigynia strongly inflated, sessile, not becoming reflexed;
          pistillate scales persistent ....7. INFLATAE
    Perigynia stipitate, not inflated; pistillate scales decidous............2. ANTHROCHLAENAE
Spikes more than 1
    Stigmas 2, achenes lenticular
        Lateral spikes sessile, short, rarely elongated,
                terminal one androgynous or gynaecandrous
        Perignia white puncticulate ....4. CANESCENTES

        Perigynia not white puncticulate
          Spikes androgynous ....12. STENORHYNCHAE

          Spikes gynaecandrous
             Perigynia narrowly to broadly wing-margined ....9. OVALES

            Perigynia at most thin-edged ....11. STELLULATAE
        Lateral spikes elongated, peduncled or sessile,
                terminal spike staminate ....1. ACUTAE

    Stigmas 3, achenes triangular
        Perigynia more or less pubescent
          Pistillate spikes with few to about 25 perigynia ....8. MONTANAE

          Pistillate spikes with very many perigynia ....6. HIRTAE
        Perigynia glabrous
          Style jointed with achene, at length
            withering and deciduous
          Lowest bract strongly sheathing ....5. FRIGIDAE

          Lowest bract sheathless or very short-sheathing ....3. ATRATAE

        Style continuous with achene, indurated persistent ....10. PHYSOCARPAE

Section 1. ACUTAE

Culms, low, arising singly or in small clumps, strongly
        stoloniferous; lowest bract normally much shorter than
        inflorescence; scales with obsolete or slender midvein
    Dried first-year leaf-blades at base of fertile culms stiff, rigid
        and conspicuous, concealing the culms; fertile culm leaves all
        blade-bearing, lower sheaths not purplish
        or hispidulous dorsally...24. *C. scopulorum*

    Dried first-year leaf-blades at base of fertile culms much
        desiccated, not stiff, rigid or conspicuous, not concealing
        the culms; lowest fertile culm leaves (of season's growth)
        not blade-bearing, lower sheaths purplish,
        more or less strongly hispidulous ....11. *C. gymnoclada*

Culms taller, less stiff, in larger clumps; lowest bract usually
        equaling or exceeding inflorescence; scales with slender
        midvein or broader light-colored center
    Peringynia strongly nerved ventrally, the nerves
        raised, strongly stipitate ....16. *C. kelloggii*

    Perigynia nerveless ventrally or with
        obscure impressed nerves ....3. *C. aquatilis*

Section 2. ANTHROCHLAENAE

Short-stoloniferous; blades flat, 1:5 mm or more wide;
  staminate flowers conspicuous; perigynia early
  spreading or deflexed ....19. *C. nigricans*

Section 3. ATRATAE

Culms few-leaved, purplish-tinged at base,
  lower culm leaves much reduced ....26. *C. spectabilis*

Culms many-leaved, clothed at base with dried-up leaves of
  previous year, brownish tinged at base ....29. *C. tolmiei*

Section 4. CANESCENTES

Spikes gynaecandrous, many-flowered; perigynia plano-convex,
  appressed-ascending, scarcely beaked, with emarginate or entire
  orifice, broadest near middle; plant glaucous;
  leaf-blades 2-4 mm wide ....7. *C. canescens*

Section 5. FRIGIDAE

Perigynia compressed-triangular, beak minutely bidentate;
  pistillate spikes linear-oblong ....1. *C. ablata*

Section 6. HIRTAE

Perigynia hairy, teeth 0.5 mm long; leaves
  glabrous, phyllopodic ....20. *C. oregonensis*

Section 7. INFLATAE

Scales 1-nerved; perigynia ovoid, inflated, tapering at apex;
  staminate part of spike scarcely conspicuous;
  achenes 1.25 mm long ....8. *C. engelmannii*

Scales 3-nerved; perigynia broadly ovoid, strongly inflated,
  very abruptly short-beaked; staminate part of spike
  conspicuous; achenes 2 mm long ....6. *C. breweri*

Section 8. MONTANAE

Basal spikes not developed ....13. *C. inops*

Basal spikes present ....5. *C. brevipes*

Section 9. OVALES

Beak of perigynium flat, serrulate to the often
        strongly bidentate tip
  Scales brownish with greenish midvein ....4. *C. brevior*

  Scales strongly reddish-brown with lighter midvein ....27. *C. straminiformis*

Beak of perigynium terete toward the apex; upper 1-3 mm smooth
        or nearly so (except in *C. preslii* and *subfusca*)
  Perigynia lanceolate, 5-5.5 mm long, 3-4 times as long as
        wide (scales equaling and narrower than perigynia;
        spikes 6-12, capitate) ....25. *C. specifica*

Perigynia ovate or broader, or if lanceolate
    shorter than 5 mm in length
  Perigynia appressed, nearly or entirely covered by scales,
    the beaks not conspicuous in the spikes
    Perigynium oblong-ovate, rather sharply margined ....21. *C. phaeocephala*

    Perigynium linear-lanceolate, very narrowly margined,
      boat-shaped ....18. *C. leporinella*

  Upper part of perigynia conspicuous in the spikes,
    not covered by the scales
  Perigynia with thinnish submembranaceous walls
    (perigynia ovate, strongly margined,
    appressed, 3.75-5 mm long)..10. *C. festivella*

  Perigynia plano-convex, walls thick, firm; nerveless
    or inconspicuously nerved on inner face
  Perigynia very small, 2.5-3.5 mm long
    Margins of perigynia entire ....14. *C. integra*

    Margins of perigynia strongly serrulate (leaf-
      blades light green, 1.5-3mm wide) ....28. *C. subfusca*

  Perigynia larger, 3.5 mm or more in length (beaks at tip
    and the scales reddish or reddish-brown-tinged) ....22. *C. preslii*

Section 10. PHYSOCARPAE

Perigynia ascending; lower sheaths somewhat filamentose;
    rootstocks short-creeping with short ascending stolons;
    leaves weakly nodulose
  Perigynia 5-7 mm long, abruptly contracted into beak ....30. *C. vesicaria*

  Perigynia 7-10 mm long, tapering into beak ....9. *C. exsiccata*
Perigynia spreading at maturity; lower sheaths not filamentose;
    densely cespitose, with long horizontal stolons;
    leaves strongly nodulose ....23. *C. rostrata*

Section 11. STELLULATAE

Spikes in a small (6-10 mm long), densely capitate,
    brownish-black head ....12. *C. illota*

Spikes widely separate, not brownish-black
  Beak of perigynium with few weak serrulations,
    the body broadest near middle ....17. *C. laeviculmis*

  Beak of perigynium strongly serrulate,
    the body broadest near base ....2. *C. angustior*

Section 12. STENORHYNCHAE

Perigynia 3-4 mm long, beak much shorter than body;
    scales dark brown ....15. *C. jonesii*

1. **Carex ablata** Bailey, Bot. Gaz. 13:82. 1888. COLD-LOVING SEDGE. Culms clustered, 20-60 cm high, much longer than the leaves; blades 3-4 mm wide, flat, sheaths loose; bracts short, long-sheathing; spikes 3-7, long-ovate to oblong, mostly narrowed at both ends, 10-20 mm long, the upper clustered and sessile, the lower widely separated and on slender peduncles. Terminal spike mostly or entirely staminate, the lateral (lower) ones staminate at apex, pistillate below; pistillate scales ovate, obtuse, very dark reddish-brown with lighter midvein and hyaline margins, shorter than the perigynia. Perigynia broadly lanceolate, greenish, about 4 mm long, 1.25 mm wide, rounded base, stipitate, the beak short, serrulate, minutely bidentate; achenes triangular; stigmas 3.

Occasional in moist meadows. H and C. McKenzie Pass area; Green Lakes 1890 m(6500 ft); Three Creek L.

2. **Carex angustior** Mackenzie in Rydb. Flora Rocky Mts. 124. 1917. NARROWER SEDGE. Culms densely tufted, 15-35 cm high, erect, slender, sharp-angled, smooth; leaves mostly shorter than the culms, 0.5-2.5 mm wide, scabrous above, flat, tapering; spikes 3-5, separated, 8-15-flowered, forming an inflorescence 1.5-4 cm long; scales light brown with green midvein, cuspidate, ovate, shorter and narrower than the body of the perigynia; perigynia broadly lanceolate, 2.5 mm or more long, tapering to a serrulate bidentate beak, slightly more than half as long as the body; achenes lenticular; stigmas 2.

Infrequent in wet meadows. Lower H to T. Melakwa L. 1555 m (5100 ft).

3. **Carex aquatilis** Wahl. in Vet. Akad. Nya Handl. Stockholm 24:165. 1803. WATER SEDGE. Cespitose; stolons horizontal, long, slender, scaly; culms 20-40 cm high, smooth, roughened above and sharply triangular; leaves shorter than the inflorescence; blades 2-5 mm wide, flat or channeled at base, light green, roughened on upper half; terminal spike staminate, narrow; lateral spikes 2-4, pistillate or the upper sometimes androgynous, 1-4 cm long, about 4 mm wide; bracts with black auricles; scales mostly acute, purplish-black, lighter midvein not evident; perigynia 2.5-3 mm long, elliptic to obovate, light green, dark glandular-dotted, stipitate, abruptly short-beaked; beak dark, entire; achenes lenticular, jointed with the short style; stigmas 2.

Infrequent in swampy meadows. H to T. Green Lakes 2000 m (6550 ft).

4. **Carex brevior** (Dewey) Mack., Bull. Torrey Club 42:605. 1915. SHORTER-BEAKED SEDGE. Cespitose, culms 20-40 cm high, erect, stiff, 3-angled; blades 2-4 mm wide, flat, much shorter than the culms; head of 3-5 or more closely aggregated spikes, the staminate flowers below the pistillate, the lowest bract short; scales shorter than the perigynia, ovate, mostly acute, brown with greenish midvein and hyaline margins; perigynia broadly ovate to suborbicular, about 4 mm long, plano-convex, thick, greenish, broadly winged, abruptly narrowed into a flat, serrulate, bidentate beak about 1 mm long; achenes lenticular; stigmas 2.

Occasional in meadows. H to T. Green Lakes 2000 m (6550 ft); Three Creek L.

5. **Carex brevipes** W. Boott, in S. Wats. Bot. Calif. 2:246. 1880. SHORT SEDGE. Cespitose; dense matted rootstocks; culms 5-15 cm high; blades about 2 mm wide, roughened toward the apex, longer than the culms; staminate spike solitary, sessile or nearly so, 5-10 mm long; pistillate spikes 3-5, the upper approximate, sessile, the lower long-peduncled; lowest bract leaf-like, extending above the culm; scales acute to cuspidate, red-brown-tinged, green center with lighter border; perigynia 2.5-3 mm long, green, puberulent, stipitate, the beak 0.25-0.75 mm long, ciliate-serrulate, bidentate, slightly colored; achenes triangular with convex sides; style short, jointed with achene; stigmas 3.

Infrequent in dry open woods. H to T. McKenzie Pass area; Camp Agoseris 1890 m (6200 ft).

6. **Carex breweri** Boott, Ill. Carex 4:142, pl. 455. 1867. BREWER'S SEDGE. Cespitose, the culms erect from a slender branching rootstock, 10-25 cm high; leaves stiff, slender, folded and appearing terete, about equaling or shorter than the culms; spike solitary, ovoid, 1-2 cm long, usually bractless, the upper part staminate, the lower pistillate; scales ovate, shorter and narrower than the perigynia, 3-nerved; perigynia strongly inflated, broadly ovate, light brown, about 5 mm long, abruptly beaked, glabrous; stigmas 3.

Common on dry sandy slopes, sometimes in moist places. A. Black Crater; Middle Sister; Wickiup Plain; Ball Butte, summit; Broken Top; Three Creek L.

7. **Carex canescens** L. Sp. Pl. 974. 1753. HOARY SEDGE. Closely cespitose, the culms slender, roughened above, mostly longer than the leaves; leaves glaucous, flat, 2-3 mm wide, pale green, attenuate, margins rough; spikes 5 more or less, somewhat remote, oblong, 5-10 mm long; bract of the lowest spike usually present; scales thin light brown with green keel, ovate, acute, slightly shorter than the perigynia; perigynia narrowly-ovate, about 2 mm long, spongy at base, minutely beaked; stigmas 2.

Occasional in wet meadows east of divide. C. Trout Cr. Swamp 1355 m (4450 ft).

A *Carex kelloggii;* **B** *Carex breweri;* **C** *Carex inops;* **D** *Carex ablata*

8. Carex engelmannii Bailey, Proc. Am. Acad. 22:132. 1886. ENGELMANN'S SEDGE. Culms loosely cespitose from slender, tough, elongated rootstocks, 8-15 cm high; leaf-blades filiform, terete, slender, shorter than the culms; sheaths loose, scarious; spike solitary, 7-10 mm long, ovoid, androgynous, densely flowered, the lower ¾ pistillate; scales 1-nerved, ovate, acute, thin, shorter than the perigynia except the lower ones; perigynia 4.5 mm long, thin, little inflated, flat, rounded at base, glabrous, nerveless, tapering to minute beak which is smooth and finally 2-toothed; achenes triangular; stigmas 3.

Rare on high rocky slopes. A and H. Middle Sister.

9. Carex exsiccata Bailey, Mem. Torrey Club 1:6. 1889. WESTERN INFLATED SEDGE. Short-creeping rhizomes; culms 35-75 cm high, sharp-angled, rough above; leaves and leaf-like bracts longer than the culms; the blades about 4 mm wide; sheaths filamentose; upper spikes staminate, 1-4, narrow, about 2-5 cm long; pistillate spikes 1-3, remote, about sessile, cylindric, 2-5 cm long, 1 cm wide; flowers many, dense; scales lance-ovate, acute, much shorter and narrower than the perigynia; perigynia lanceolate, 7-10 mm long, little inflated, smooth, strongly veined, tapering into a long, smooth beak, deeply bidentate; achenes triangular; style slender and continuous with the achene; stigmas 3.

Occasional in wet ground. Lower H to T. Melakwa L. 1495 m (4900 ft); McKenzie Pass area.

10. Carex festivella Mack., Bull. Torrey Club 42:609. 1915. MOUNTAIN MEADOW SEDGE. Cespitose; rootstocks with very dark fibrous scales; culms 25-50 cm high, smooth except below the head, slender, 3-angled; leaf-blades 2-4 mm wide, shorter than the culms; head ovoid of 5-10 or more spikes densely aggregated, 10-20 mm long; bracts short, not longer than the head; spikes gynaecandrous; scales shorter than the perigynia, ovate, acute, brown; perigynia light brown and greenish, thin, flat, ovate, winged, tapering into a serrulate beak, minutely bidentate; achenes lenticular; style slender and jointed with achene; stigmas 2.

Frequent in moist meadows. H to T. McKenzie Pass; Scott Mt.; Trout Cr. Swamp; Soda Cr.

11. Carex gymnoclada Holm, Am. Journ. Sci. IV. 14:424. f. 12-14. 1902. SIERRA ALPINE SEDGE. Stoloniferous; culms 15-45 cm high, roughened or smooth above, stiff, sharply triangular, phyllopodic; leaves little shorter than culms; blades 2.5-4 mm wide, light green, flat, rough margins; bracts with small to quite long, black auricles; scales obtuse to acute, black with light midvein and hyaline margins; perigynia 2.5-3 mm by 1.5 mm, granular, 2-ribbed, pale at base, dark at apex, abruptly narrowed to outward-curved beak; beak 0.1-0.25 mm long, entire, light or dark; achenes lenticular, jointed with the short style; stigmas 2.

Infrequent in moist ground. A and H. Fall Cr. near Sparks L. 1670 m (5475 ft).

12. Carex illota Bailey, Mem. Torrey Club 1:15. 1889. SMALL-HEADED SEDGE. Cespitose, the rootstocks covered with brown fibrous scales; culms erect, 10-30 cm high, smooth except roughened below the head, much longer than the leaves; blades short, flat, 1:5-3 mm wide; basal sheaths dark brown; spikes 3-5, gynaecandrous or pistillate, forming a dense ovate head 6-10 mm long; bracts not developed; scales brown, ovate, obtuse, shorter than the perigynia; perigynia ovate, 3 mm long, smooth, nerved, beak about one-third length of body, emarginate, the base rounded, spongy; achenes lenticular; stigmas 2.

Occasional in meadows. H. West Lava Camp; Lake Valley; Three Creek L.; Green Lakes.

13. Carex inops Bailey, Proc. Am. Acad. 22:126. 1886. LONG-STOLONED SEDGE. Cespitose, strongly stoloniferous, the under-ground parts covered with fibrous, light-red-brown scales; culms roughened above, 15-30 cm high, longer than the leaves, slender; leaves clustered at the base, 1.5-3 mm wide; margins and upper surface very rough; lowest bract about as long as the spike; the staminate (upper) spike solitary, scales about 1.5 cm long, reddish-brown with white hyaline margin; pistillate spikes 1-3, mostly approximate, 7-12 mm long, half as wide; perigynia few, 2.5 mm long or longer, nearly globose, pubescent, stipitate, abruptly beaked, the beak deeply bidentate; scales ovate, sharp-pointed, reddish-brown with wide hyaline margin and green center stripe; achenes triangular, closely enclosed; style short, jointed with the achene; stigmas 3, long.

Occasional in dry open woods. H to T. Black Crater 2215 m (7260 ft); McKenzie Pass; Frog Camp; Green Lakes Tr. at 1830 m (6000 ft).

14. Carex integra Mackenzie Bull. Torrey Club. 43:608. 1917. SMOOTH-BEAKED SEDGE. Densely cespitose; culms 15-30 cm high, slender, smooth; leaves 1-2 mm wide, margins scabrous, shorter than the culms; bracts undeveloped; spikes 5-10, gynaecandrous, crowded into a narrowly ovoid head about 2 cm long; scales long-ovate, acute, light midvein and margins, about as long as the perigynia; perigynia small, lanceolate, plano-convex, base tapered, beak slender, smooth; achenes lenticular, jointed with the style; stigmas 2.

Rare in open woods. Lower H to T. West Lava Camp 1535 m (5036 ft).

15. Carex jonesii Bailey, Mem. Torrey Club 1:16. 1889. JONES' SEDGE. Cespitose; culms 15-35 cm high, exceeding the leaves, upper half roughened; leaves clustered at base, 2-4 mm wide, margins scabrous; bracts not developed; spikes androgynous, 5 or more in a compact broadly ovoid head, 10-16 mm long; scales ovoid, dark brown, little longer or shorter than the perigynia; perigynia ovate-lanceolate, plano-convex, 3-4 mm long; rounded base, short stipitate, many-nerved dorsally, tapering into a nearly smooth, bidentate beak, about one-third length of body; achenes lenticular; stigmas 2, short.

Rare in wet meadows. C. Trout Cr. Swamp.

16. Carex kelloggii W. Boott, in S. Wats. Bot. Calif. 2:240. 1880. KELLOGG'S SEDGE. Cespitose; rhizomes stout creeping; culms 25-60 cm high, roughened above, mostly shorter than the leaves, slender; staminate spike slender, cylindric, 2-3 cm long, often solitary or with 2-3 shorter ones clustered at its base; scales dark red-brown with light center stripe; pistillate spikes 2-6, more or less distant, especially the lowest; scales smaller than the perigynia, dark red-brown with broad, greenish center stripe; perigynia 2.5 mm long, half as wide, nerved, granulose, strongly stipitate, abruptly short beaked, the beak entire, dark-colored; achenes lenticular; stigmas 2.

Common in wet meadows. Lower H to T. Lava Camp L.; McKenzie Pass; Lake Valley; Melakwa L.; Spring L.; Sparks L.

17. Carex laeviculmis Meinsh. Bot. Contralbl. 55:195. 1893. SMOOTH-STEMMED SEDGE. Cespitose; rootstocks slender; culms 30-60 cm high, slender, weak, roughened above; leaves shorter than the culms; blades 1.5-2 mm wide, soft, light green; spikes gynaecandrous, remote, mostly under 10 mm long; lowest bract developed; perigynia 4-8, ovoid, plano-convex, 2.5 mm long, tapering into beak about one-third length of body, serrulate, bidentate; achenes lenticular; stigmas 2.

Rare in wet ground. Lower H to T. Spring L. 1555 m (5100 ft).

18. Carex leporinella Mackenzie Bull. Torrey Club. 43:605. 1917. SIERRA HARE SEDGE. Densely cespitose; rootstocks short, fibrillose; culms 15-30 cm high, stiff, smooth; leaves from near the base; blades 0.75-1.5 mm wide, green, involute, roughened toward apex; spikes gynaecandrous, forming a head 1.5-3 mm long; bracts scale-like or the lower prolonged; scales acute, reddish-brown with lighter midvein and margins; staminate flowers few; perigynia linear-lanceolate, 3.5-4 mm long, concealed by scales, plano-convex, wing-margined, serrulate above; beak 1 mm long, serrulate below; achenes lenticular, jointed with the style; stigmas 2, long.

Appears to be rare, on rocky slopes. A and H. Little Brother above 1890 m (6500 ft).

19. Carex nigricans C. A. Meyer, Mem. Acad. St. Petersb. 1:211. pl. 7. 1831. BLACKISH SEDGE. Cespitose; rhizomes creeping; culms 5-20 cm high, slender, smooth, exceeding the leaves; blades 1.5-2.5 mm wide; spike solitary, androgynous, 10-15 mm long, 6-19 mm wide, densely flowered, without bracts; scales ovate, acute, dark brown, little shorter than the perigynia, soon deciduous; perigynia 3.5 mm long, 1 mm wide, brown, glabrous, strongly stipitate, ovate, tapering to long, smooth beak with dorsal suture; achenes triangular; stigmas 3.

Frequent in alpine meadows and open places, dry or moist. A and H. Pine Butte; Scott Mt.; Sunshine Shelter; Camp Agoseris; South Sister at 2440 m (8000 ft); Broken Top; Three Creek L.

20. Carex oregonensis Olney, Proc. Am. Acad. 8:407. 1872. OREGON SEDGE. (*C. halliana* Bailey, Bot. Gaz. 9:117. 1884). Rootstocks creeping, woody, slender; culms 15-35 cm high, stout, sharply angled, smooth; leaves phyllopodic, mostly exceeding the culms, 3-5 mm wide, stiff, scabrous on the margins, flat or folded; staminate spikes 2-3, terminal; pistillate spikes 3 or more, the lower often widely separated; lowest bract leaf-like, exceeding the culm; scales of the pistillate spike shorter than the perigynia, strongly keeled, light green with very wide hyaline margins, ovate, acute or spine-tipped; perigynia 4-5 mm long, 2-2.5 mm wide, ovoid, triangular, densely pubescent, tapering into a strongly bidentate beak; achenes triangular, jointed with the style; stigmas 3.

Frequent in open woods and meadows. H. McKenzie Pass area; Scott Mt.; White Branch Cr.; Obsidian Cliffs; Green Lakes area.

21. Carex phaeocephala Piper, Contr. U. S. Nat. Herb. 11:172. 1906. MOUNTAIN HARE SEDGE. Densely cespitose; culms 15-30 cm high, slender, roughened above, exceeding the leaves; leaves phyllopodic, 1.5-2 mm wide, partly involute, scabrous on the margins; lower bract occasionally developed; spikes 2-5, closely approximate, gynaecandrous, 6-12 mm long, forming a variously shaped head; scales broadly lanceolate, brown with light green midvein and hyaline margins, covering the perigynia; perigynia oblong-ovate, 4 mm long, 1.5 mm wide, greenish and brown, winged, rounded base, strongly nerved dorsally, upper half serrulate, tapering into the 1 mm long beak; achenes lenticular; stigmas 2.

Occasional on open slopes. A and H. Pine Butte; Scott Mt. Trail; Frog Camp; Ball Butte 2440 m (8000 ft).

22. Carex preslii Steud. Synops. Cyper. 242. 1855. PRESL'S SEDGE. Densely cespitose; culms 20-40 cm high, roughened above, slender, exceeding the leaves; blades 1-2.5 mm wide, flat; head 12-20 mm long, 8-12 mm wide; spikes 3-8, ovoid, gynaecandrous, closely aggregated; bracts not developed; scales brown with lighter midvein and margins, about covering the perigynia, acute; perigynia 3.5 mm long, 1.5 mm wide, ovate, distended, greenish to brown, narrow-winged and serrulate above, the beak 1 mm long, closely bidentate; achenes lenticular, jointed with the style; stigmas 2.

Occasional in dry open woods. H and C. McKenzie Pass area; Obsidian Cliffs 1890 m (6200 ft); Green Lakes; Fall Cr. trail.

23. Carex rostrata Stokes in With. Arrang. Brit. Pl. ed. 2, 2:1059. 1787. BEAKED SEDGE. Cespitose; culms 40-60 cm high, rough above the first spike; leaves much longer than the inflorescence, flat, 4-12 mm wide, distinctly nodulose, rough on the margins; bracts very long, the lower exceeding the inflorescence; upper spikes staminate, 2-4, slender, about 4 mm wide; lower spikes pistillate, 2-4, remote, cylindric, densely many-flowered; scales lanceolate, very narrow, about as long as the perigynia, red-brown with light center, attenuate; perigynia ovoid, about 5 mm long, inflated, smooth, greenish to light brown; beak 1 mm or more long, distinctly bidentate, the teeth 0.5 mm long; achenes triangular, with the style continuous; stigmas 3.

Rare in swamps. Lower H to T. McKenzie Pass area.

24. Carex scopulorum Holm, Am. Journ. Sci. IV. 14:421-2. f. 1-6. 1902. HOLM'S ROCKY MOUNTAIN SEDGE. Stoloniferous; culms single or few in loose clusters. 15-50 cm high, stiff, rough above; leaves phyllopodic, usually shorter than culms, 3-6 mm wide; terminal spike staminate or androgynous; lateral spikes 2-3, pistillate or androgynous, approximate, erect, mostly sessile, 1-2 cm long, 6 mm wide; bracts shorter than inflorescence, red-brown auricled; scales broadly ovate, black, about equaling the perigynia, midvein scarcely evident; perigynia about 3 mm long, papillose, greenish straw-colored becoming dark reddish-brown and more or less mottled, spreading, inflated, abruptly contracted into a short beak, entire, recurved; achenes lenticular; style slender; stigmas 2.

Frequent in wet meadows. H to A. West Lava Camp; Camp Agoseries; Devil's L.; Green Lakes; Three Creek L.

25. Carex specifica Bailey, Mem. Torrey Club 1:21. 1889. NARROW-FRUITED SEDGE. Densely cespitose; culms 30-50 cm high, erect, stiff, smooth, greatly exceeding the phyllopodic leaves; blades 2-4 mm wide, canaliculate; head capitate, about 1.5 cm long, 1.25 cm wide, of 6 or more spikes closely aggregated; spikes gynaecandrous, oblong; bracts not developed; scales long-ovate, attenuate, shorter than the perigynia, dark brown with lighter midvein; parigynia lanceolate, about 5.5 mm long, 1.5 mm wide, many-nerved both surfaces, plano-convex, greenish to straw-colored, narrow margined, serrulate above, tapering to a long beak, bidentate, reddish-brown-tipped; achenes lenticular, jointed with the slender style; stigmas 2.

Rare in meadows. H. Three Creek L.

26. Carex spectabilis Dewey, Am. Journ. Sci. 29:248. pl. 10, f. 76. 1836. SHOWY SEDGE. Cespitose, 30-50 cm high; culms slender, sharply triangular; lower culm-leaves with short blades; leaf-blades 2-5 mm wide; terminal spike and often the one next below, staminate; pistillate spikes 2-4, erect, oblong, 1-2.5 cm long, 3-5 mm wide, the upper short-peduncled, aggregated, the lowest distant, long-peduncled; bracts dark-auricled, the lowest about equaling the often nodding inflorescence; scales lanceolate, purplish-black, shorter than or exceeding the perigynia, prominent, light-colored, usually excurrent midvein; perigynia oblong-ovate, 2.5-3.5 mm long, 1.5-2 mm wide, purplish-black, striated and mottled, rounded to very short scarcely bidentate beak; achenes triangular, jointed with the style; stigmas 3.

Occasional in alpine meadows. A. Near Matthieu L.; Camp Agoseries 1890 m (6200 ft); South Sister.

27. Carex straminiformis Bailey, Mem. Torrey Club 1:24. 1889. MT. SHASTA SEDGE. Densely cespitose; culms 25-50 cm high, stiff, erect, much longer than the leaves; blades 2-4 mm wide, basal sheaths light brown; head broad, 1.5-2.5 cm long; spikes 3-6, gynaecandrous, about 9 mm long, closely aggregated; bracts little developed; scales broadly-lanceolate, acute, shorter than the perigynia, bright red-brown, light midvein; perigynia broadly-ovate, 4 mm long, 3 mm wide, upper half serrulate, broadly winged to base, light brown; beak bidentate; achenes lenticular; style jointed with achene; stigmas 2.

Occasional on rocky slopes. A and H. Middle and South Sister; Wickiup Plain; Green Lakes.

28. Carex subfusca W. Boott, in S. Wats, Bot. Calif. 2:234. 1880. RUSTY SEDGE. Cespitose; culms 20-60 cm high, slender, roughened above, longer than the leaves; blades 1.5-3 mm wide; head ovoid, 1-2 cm long; spikes 4-5, gynaecandrous, aggregated; bracts little developed; scales longer than perigynia, ovate, acute, brown, lighter midvein and hyaline margin; perigynia about 3 mm long, ovate, distinctly winged to the rounded base, plano-convex, upper half serrulate; beak half as long as body, minutely bidentate, brown; achenes lenticular; style jointed with achene; stigmas 2.

Infrequent in moist places. H to C and T. Green Lakes.

29. Carex tolmiei Boott, in Hook, Fl. Bor. Am. 2:224. 1840.

TOLMIE'S SEDGE. Cespitose from creeping rhizomes; culms 15-40 cm high, much longer than the leaves, phyllopodic, triangular, slightly rough above; basal sheaths dark purplish-red, fibrillose; blades 2-4 mm wide; terminal spike staminate, 1-2 cm long, scales purplish-black, midvein light, not excurrent; pistillate spikes 2-4 or more, oblong, 10-15 mm long, closely many-flowered, approximate, the lowest often remote; bracts developed, the lowest often exceeding the inflorescence and with long red-brown auricles or sheath; scales of pistillate spikes about as long as the perigynia, purplish-black, ovate, more or less acute; perigynia oblong-ovate, 3-4 mm long, straw-colored, purplish above; beak dark, 0.5 mm long, minutely bidentate; achenes triangular; style jointed with achene; stigmas 3.

Frequent in mountain meadows. H and C. White Branch Cr.; Camp Agoseris; Sunshine Shelter 2045 m (6700 ft); South Sister, west slopes; upper Squaw Cr., at about 2135 m (7000 ft).

30. Carex vesicaria L. Sp. Pl. 979. 1753.

INFLATED CAREX. Cespitose from stout creeping rhizomes; culms 30-60 cm high, sharp-angled, rough above, shorter than the leaves, red-purplish tinged at base; blades 3-6 mm wide, nodulose, margins rough; sheaths fibrillose, nodulose; staminate spikes 2-4, well above the pistillate spikes, linear, 2-5 cm long, 2.5-5 mm wide, with shorter bracts or none; pistillate spikes 2-3, remote, about sessile, erect, oblong-cylindric, 2-6 cm long, 6-12 mm wide, many-flowered; bracts leaf-like, sheathed, very long, the lower exceeding the inflorescence; scales ovate, shorter than perigynia, acute; perigynia ovoid, 5-7 mm long, smooth, inflated, nerved; beak 2 mm long, bidentate, the teeth about 0.5 mm long, smooth, erect; achenes triangular; style continuous with achene; stigmas 3.

Frequent in swamps. Lower H to T. Trout Cr. Swamp; West Lava Camp; Scott L.; Benson-Tenas Lakes 1645 m (5400 ft).

ELEOCHARIS R. Br.

Perennial or annual; culms simple, clustered; leaves reduced to basal sheaths; spikelets solitary, erect, terete, several to many-flowered; perianth wanting or of 3-12 bristles, barbed; stamens 2-3; style 2-3-cleft, enlarged at base forming a tubercle on the apex of the lenticular or triangular achene.

KEY TO THE SPECIES OF ELEOCHARIS

Tubercle formed from base of style on the achene
    and not continuous with it
        Style 3-branched, achenes 3-sided, pale..*E. acicularis*

        Style 2-branched, achenes lenticular, smooth, yellow................................*E. palustris*

Tubercle continuous with apex of achene, culms flattened................................*E. rostellata*

Eleocharis acicularis (L.) R. & S. Syst. 2:154. 1817.

NEEDLE SPIKE-RUSH. Tufted perennial, 2-5 cm high; culms filiform; spikelet flattened, narrowly ovate, 2-5 mm long.

Occasional in wet ground. H to T. Lake Valley 1465 m (4800 ft).

Eleocharis palustris (L.) R. & S. Syst. 2:151. 1817.

CREEPING SPIKE-RUSH. Perennial by creeping rootstocks; culms mostly terete 15-25 cm high; spikelets lanceolate 6-16 mm long, 3.5 mm in diameter, thicker than the culm.

Rare in the area. Emersed or on wet shores. H to T. Craig L. 1555 m (5100 ft).

Eleocharis rostellata Torr. Fl. N. Y. 2:347. 1843.

BEAKED SPIKE-RUSH. Perennial; caudex stout; culms slender, wiry, mostly erect; spikelets 4-6 mm long; sheaths close-fitting; stamens 3; style 3-cleft; achenes obovoid, obscurely 3-angled; tubercle at top of achene less than half as long as the achene; bristles 4-8, retrorsely barbed.

Infrequent in wet ground. H to T. West Lava Camp; Green Lakes.

ERIOPHORUM L.

Eriophorum gracile Koch. Roth Catal. Bot. 2: 259. 1800. SLENDER COTTON-GRASS. Perennial by rootstocks; culms slender, 22-35 cm high; sheaths longer than the linear blunt-tipped leaves; involucral leaves shorter than the inflorescence; spikelets 1-5, terminal, drooping; perianth bristles white, 2 cm long.

Rare in this area in bogs. Lower H and C. Spring L. 1555 m (5100 ft).

SCIRPUS L.

Scirpus congdonii Britton, var. **minor** Henderson, Rhodora 32:21. 1930. CONGDON'S BULRUSH. Perennial by stout rootstocks; culms erect, glabrous, 20-35 cm high; leaves 5-8 mm wide, 9-20 cm long, smooth, shorter than the culms. Rays of umbel several, unequal; spikelets capitate, many-flowered; achenes sharply 3-angled, light brown.

Frequent in Lake Valley area in swamps and meadows. Lower H. Type locality, McKenzie Pass at about 1525 m (5000 ft), Henderson No. 7108, type.

12. JUNCACEAE   Rush Family

Mostly perennial grass-like herbs growing in marshy places. Perianth parts 6; stamens 3 or 6; pistil superior, carpels 3 united; capsule many-seeded or 3 only.

KEY TO THE GENERA OF JUNCACEAE

Capsule 1 or 3-celled, many-seeded, leaf-sheaths open..................................*Juncus*

Capsule 1-celled, 3-seeded, leaf-sheaths closed................................*Luzula*

JUNCUS L. Rush

Plants perennial or annual mostly growing in marshy places. Stems and leaves glabrous, terete, grass-like. Inflorescence paniculate or capitate; perianth parts small; stamens 3 or 6; carpels 3 united; seeds several to many.

KEY TO THE SPECIES OF JUNCUS

Inflorescence appearing lateral
  Stems tufted, inflorescence 2- or 3-flowered rarely
    more, alpine species
    Leaf-blade of the upper basal leaf-sheath well
      developed, capsule acute.....................................*J. parryi*

    Leaf-blade not developed, capsule notched at apex......................*J. drummondii*
  Stems from creeping rhizomes, inflorescence many-flowered
    Panicle simple, anthers about as long as the filaments,
      capsule broadly obovoid.....................................*J. filiformis*

    Inflorescence dense or diffuse, flowers often nodding, anthers
      much shorter than filaments, capsule narrowly ovoid..................*J. balticus*

Inflorescence not appearing lateral, flowers in capitate clusters
  Leaf-blades not septate, perianth segments with scarious
    margins, stamens 6.....................................*J. regelii*

  Leaf-blades septate, perianth segments without scarious
    margins, stamens 3 or 6
    Leaf-blades slender, slightly compressed sheaths with
      auricles, stamens 6, heads solitary.....................................*J. mertensianus*

    Leaves compressed laterally, equitant, auricles wanting,
      stamens 3, many-flowered heads in panicle.....................................*J. ensifolius*

A *Scirpus congdonii;* B *Juncus ensifolius;* C *Luzula grabrata*

Juncus balticus Willd. Berlin Mag. 3:298. 1809. BALTIC RUSH. Perennial with wiry stems from stout creeping rootstocks, 25-75 cm high; basal leaf-sheaths bladeless; leaf of the inflorescence 15-30 cm long appearing as continuation of the stem; panicle open, about 4 cm high; perianth 4.5 mm long; stamens about half as long as the perianth segments, the capsule about equaling them.

Infrequent on wet borders of lakes and streams. Lower H. Hand L.; Scott L.

Juncus drummondii Meyer; Ledeb. Fl. Ross. 4:235. 1853. DRUMMOND'S RUSH. Perennial; stems tufted, 15-30 cm high; basal leaf-sheaths without blades; inflorescence 2-3-flowered, each with 2 bractlets at base; perianth about 4.5 mm long, the segments lanceolate, brown with green center stripe; stamens 6, half the length of the perianth; capsule oblong, apex notched, equaling the perianth.

Occasional in wet places. A and H. White Branch Cr. at 1800 m (5900 ft); Green Lakes.

Juncus ensifolius Wikstr. Kongl. Vet. Akad. Handl. 2:274. 1823. THREE-STEMMED RUSH. Perennial; creeping rootstocks; stems flattened, 2-edged, 17.5-35 cm high; leaves equitant, flattened, 8-18 cm long, 4.5-8 mm wide; heads several in clusters, 3-6-flowered; perianth 3 mm long, brown, acuminate; stamens 3, ⅔ length of perianth; capsule oblong, obtuse.

Frequent in wet places. Lower H and C. West Lava Camp; Spring L.; Trout Cr. Swamp.

Juncus filiformis L. Sp. Pl. 326. 1753. THREAD RUSH. Slender creeping rootstocks; stems slender, 6.5-30 cm high; basal leaf-sheaths short, tight; leaf of inflorescence appearing as continuation of stem and usually exceeding it; 5-15-flowered panicle; perianth 3-4 mm long, acute; stamens 6, half as long; capsule obovoid, shorter than the perianth.

Occasional on wet borders of lakes and streams. Lower H and C. Scott L.; Melakwa L.; West Lava Camp.

Juncus mertensianus Bong. Mem. Acad. St. Petersb. VI. 2:167. 1832. MERTEN'S RUSH. Short matted rootstocks; stems slender 7.5-30 cm high; 2-3 stem leaves equaling or shorter than the stem, auricles on sheaths; heads usually solitary, many flowered, 3-9 mm broad; perianth 3 mm long, dark brown; stamens 6, nearly equaling the perianth; anthers shorter than the filaments; capsule oblong, mucronate, about as long as the perianth.

Common in moist places. A to C. Lake Valley; Green Lakes; Wickiup Plain 1922 m (6300 ft); Park Meadow 1875 m (6150 ft).

Juncus parryi Engelm. Trans. St. Louis Acad. 2:446. 1866. PARRY'S RUSH. Stems tufted, 7.5-25 cm high, slender; rootstocks matted; leaves terete, half or less as long as the stems; flowers 2-3, each with pair of bracts; perianth about 6.5 mm long, light brown or green, wide scarious margins, segments lanceolate; stamens 6, half the length of the perianth, the anthers much longer than the filaments; capsule oblong, acute.

Common in dry grassy meadows and open woods. A to C. Pine Butte 1675 m (5500 ft); Middle Sister at 2290 m (7500 ft); Sparks L.

Juncus regelii Buch. Engler Bot. Jahrb. 12:414. 1890. REGEL'S RUSH. Rootstocks stout; stems tufted, slender, 12-30 cm high; stem-leaves usually 3, grasslike; heads 1-8, several-flowered; perianth 4-5 mm long, minutely roughened, the segments brown with green center stripe; stamens 6, ⅔ length of segments; anthers equal to filaments; capsule ovoid, little shorter than perianth.

Infrequent in wet ground. H and C. Soda Creek at 1740 m (5700 ft); Trout Cr. Swamp 1355 m (4450 ft).

LUZULA D C. Wood-rush

Perennials with slender hollow stems; leaves flat, soft grass-like with closed sheaths.

KEY TO THE SPECIES OF LUZULA

Flowers in 1-several spike-like clusters..*L. campestris*
Flowers in open panicle
    Panicle branches divaricate, leaves glabrous................................*L. glabrata*
    Panicle branches slender lax and drooping, leaves sparsely
       pilose on the sheaths and margins................................*L. piperi*

Luzula campestris (L.) DC. Fl. Fr. 3:161. 1805. COMMON WOOD-RUSH. Densely tufted, 10-25 cm high; leaves 3-6 mm wide, linear-lanceolate tapering to blunt gland-like tip, sparsely long-villous at the margins and sheaths; inflorescence umbellate clusters of short spikes; perianth 2 mm long, brown; capsule about as long as the perianth.

Frequent in open woods and meadows. A to AT. Lake Valley; Park Meadow 1875 m (6150 ft).

Luzula glabrata (Hoppe) Desv. Journ. de Bot. 1:145. 1808. SMOOTH WOOD-RUSH. Rootstocks long, scaly; stems 15-35 cm high; leaves smooth, shiny above, 6-11 mm wide, 7.5-15 cm long, acute; basal leaves longer; panicles open, spreading, many-flowered; perianth 2-3 mm long, acute, dark reddish-brown; capsule equaling or longer than perianth.

Common in woods. H. Black Crater 1830-2215 m (6000-7260 ft); Sunshine Shelter 2045 m (6700 ft); Green Lakes.

Luzula piperi (Coville) M. E. Jones, Bull. Montana Biol. Ser. 15:22. 1910. PIPER'S WOOD-RUSH. Densely tufted, stems 15-35 cm high; leaves mostly basal, linear-lanceolate, sparsely long-villous at the sheaths, dull green, 3-4.5 mm wide, much shorter than the stem; panicle open, drooping; flowers mostly borne singly; perianth 1.5-2 mm long, dark reddish-brown; capsule longer than the perianth.

Occasional in woods and open places. A and H. Middle Sister, west slope at 2440 m (8000 ft); Black Crater; Green Lakes.

13. LILIACEAE   Lily Family

Herbs, mostly perennial from bulbs, corms or rootstocks; leaves parallel- or net-veined; floral parts in 3's; ovary superior, 3-celled; fruit a capsule or berry.

KEY TO THE GENERA OF LILIACEAE

Fruit a capsule not fleshy
  Plants with bulbs or corms, styles 1 entire or parted,
      perianth segments united or distinct
    Perianth segments dissimilar, the outer narrower........................*Calochortus*

    Perianth segments similar
      Leaves 2, rarely 3, basal..*Erythronium*

      Leaves several, caulescent
        Perianth companulate, leaves mostly scattered, style 3-parted...........*Fritillaria*

        Perianth not companulate, leaves in whorls, style entire.....................*Lilium*

  Plants with rootstocks, styles 3 distinct, perianth
      segments distinct
  Leaves equitant..*Tofieldia*

  Leaves not equitant
    Leaves mostly basal, numerous, long, narrow, stiff;
      flowers in a terminal receme..*Xerophyllum*

    Leaves not basal; large, broad, plaited, flowers
      in a terminal panicle...*Veratrum*

Fruit a fleshy capsule or berry
  Plants with a single flower
    Leaves 2-3 all basal, fruit a berry....................................*Clintonia*

    Leaves 3 in a whorl just below the flower,
      fruit a fleshy capsule..*Trillium*

  Plants with several to many flowers
    Flowers 1-2 in the axils of leaves....................................*Streptopus*

    Flowers in a terminal receme or panicle...............................*Smilacina*

CALOCHORTUS Pursh

Calochortus lobbii (Baker) Purdy, Proc. Calif. Acad. III. 2:122. 1901. CASCADE (ALPINE) CAT'S EAR. MARIPOSA LILY. Stems erect, slender, 15-20 cm high; single leaf, linear-lanceolate, 5-10 mm wide; flowers 2-6 on pedicels; sepals lanceolate, cream-white with dark purple spot near inner base; petals cream-white, broadly obovate 15-25 mm long, sparsely long-hairy within, purple gland near base.

Frequent, loose sandy soil in open woods. H. Mc-Kenzie Pass area; Frog Camp; Linton Cr. head-waters 1830 m (6000 ft) ; Park Meadow.

CLINTONIA Raf.

Clintonia uniflora (Schult.) Kunth. Enum. 5:159. 1850. ONE-FLOWERED CLINTONIA. Rootstocks slender creeping; stems slender 6-9 cm high; leaves 2-3 basal, pale beneath, 10-15 cm long, oblanceolate; flowers usually solitary, white; perianth segments obtuse, to 2 cm long; berry blue 9-12 mm in diameter.

Infrequent in damp woods. Lower H to T. West Lava Camp; Hand L.; Spring L. 1556 m (5100 ft).

ERYTHRONIUM L.

Erythronium grandiflorum Pursh, var. **pallidum** St. John. Research Stud. St. Col. Wash. 2:113. 1931. LAMB'S TONGUE. FAWN LILY. Low herb; corm oblong, deep-seated; stem simple 15-40 cm high; 2 leaves near base lance-oblong, 10-15 cm long, acute, gradually narrowing to petioles; flowers 1-3; perianth yellow; anthers white; capsule narrow-oblong.

Very rare in woods in this area. H and C. Skyline Tr. west slope Middle Sister 1980 m (6500 ft).

FRITILLARIA L.

Fritillaria atropurpurea Nutt. Jour. Acad. Philad. 7:54. 1834. PURPLE RICE-ROOT LILY. Bulb with fleshy scales; stem 15-30 cm high; leaves scattered on upper part of stem, linear, 7-10 cm long; flowers 1-4, brownish-purple mottled yellowish; capsule obovoid, acutely angled.

Infrequent in dry woods eastern side only. C and AT. Trout Cr. Butte 1675 m (5500 ft) ; Trout Cr. Swamp.

LILIUM L.

Lilium washingtonianum Kell. Proc. Calif. Acad. 2:13. 1863. CASCADE LILY. Bulb 15-20 cm long, imbricated white, fleshy scales; stem 45-90 cm high; leaves in whorls of 6 or more, narrowly elliptic, acute, 5-10 cm long; flowers 2 to several in a receme; perianth-segments 6-9 cm long, white with fine dots, turning purplish with age, vary fragrant; capsule about 3 cm long.

Occasional in dry sandy places and open woods. Lower H to T. Sand Hills; Tenas L.; Sims Butte at 1555 m (5635 ft) ; Black Crater.

SMILACINA Desf.

Flowers numerous in a panicle...S. amplexicaulis
Flowers few in a raceme..S. sessilifolia

Smilacina amplexicaulis Nutt. Journ. Acad. Philad. 7:58. 1834. WESTERN FALSE SOLOMON'S SEAL. Rootstock stout, narrow; stem simple, puberulent, ascending, 50-90 cm high; leaves broadly lanceolate, 6.5-13 cm long, acuminate, sessile or clasping, puberulent; pedicels short; perianth-segments white, 2 mm long; berries globose, red-mottled, 5 mm in diameter.

Infrequent in woods. Lower H to T. McKenzie Pass area; Windy Point.

Smilacina stellata L. (Desf.) var. **sessiliofolia** (Baker) Henderson, Bull. Torrey Club 27:358. 1900. FEW-FLOWERED FALSE SOLOMON'S SEAL. Rootstock slender; stem 15-50 cm high, usually glabrous; leaves broadly lanceolate, 6-12 cm long, acuminate, sessile and clasping, puberulent beneath; raceme open, few-flowered; perianth-segments white, about 5 mm long; berries globose, dark red, about 7 mm in diameter.

Infrequent in woods. Lower H to T. Hand L.; Windy Point.

STREPTOPUS Michx.

Stems branched, flowers greenish-white...S. amplexifolius
Stems simple, flowers red-purple..S. curvipes

Streptopus amplexifolius (L.) DC. Fl. France 3:174. 1805. LARGE TWISTED-STALK. Rootstock horizontal; stem usually branched, 40-90 cm high, glabrous; leaves ovate to lanceolate, clasping, 8-15 cm long, glabrous, glaucous beneath; peduncles long,

filiform, sharply bent above the middle, 1-2-flowered; perianth-segments lanceolate, spreading, about 1.5 cm long; stigma entire, truncate; berries oval, red, about 12 mm in diameter.

Rare in moist woods. T. Trout Cr. Swamp.

A *Tofieldia occidentalis;* **B** *Habenaria leucostachys;* **C** *Spiranthes romanzoffiana;*
D *Calochortus lobbii*

Streptopus curvipes Vail, Bull. Torrey Club 28:267. 1902. SMALLER TWISTED-STALK. Rootstock slender, roots few; stem simple, 10-25 cm high; leaves oblong-lanceolate, acuminate, sessile, 5-10 cm long, glabrous, margins ciliate; perianth 5-7 mm long; fruit globose, red, 7-9 mm in diameter.

Rare in moist woods. Lower H to HT. West Lava Camp; Spring L.; Soda Cr. at 1740 m (5700 ft).

TOFIELDIA Huds.

Perenials with short rootstocks; leaves linear, equitant, in basal cluster; stamens 6; ovary and capsule 3-lobed.

Tofieldia occidentalis Wats. Proc. Am. Acad. 14:283. 1879. WESTERN TOFIELDIA. Stems slender, 15-50 cm high, upper parts viscid; leaves mostly basal, 10-30 cm long, 3-6 mm wide; inflorescence narrow, pedicels in clusters of 3; perianth pale yellow, segments oblong, 4 mm long; capsule tipped with 3 recurved styles.

Frequent in moist meadows and marshes. H. West Lava Camp; Green Lakes; South Sister at 1830 m (6000 ft); Todd L.

TRILLIUM L.

Trillium ovatum Pursh, Fl. Am. Sept. 245. 1814. WESTERN TRILLIUM. Herb about 25 cm high; rootstock fleshy; leaves 3 in whorl at summit of unbranched stem, rhombic-ovate 5-13 cm long, sessile; flower solitary on peduncle, 4-6 cm long; petals white, elliptic, 3-5 cm long; sepals green, broadly lanceolate, shorter than the petals; capsule broadly ovoid, slightly winged.

Rare in woods. Lower H. Mostly C and T. West Lava Camp; Trout Cr. Swamp.

VERATRUM L.

Tall perennials; rootstocks thick; leaves broad, plainted.

Veratrum viride Ait. Hort. Kew. 3:422. 1789.

GREEN FALSE HELLEBORE. Stems 1-1.5 m high, pubescent; leaves numerous, broadly oval, strongly veined and plaited, 20-30 cm long, 9-20 cm wide; panicle large, spreading; flowers yellowish-green, oblong segments 8-10 mm long; stamens half as long; capsule thick; seeds many.

Occasional in wet meadows. H. Scott L.; South Sister; Todd L.; Green Lakes.

XEROPHYLLUM Michx.

Xerophyllum tenax (Pursh) Nutt. Gen. 1:235. 1818. BEAR-GRASS. SQUAW-GRASS. Rootstock thick, woody; stem solitary, stout, 45-125 cm high; basal leaves grass-like, long rigid with rough margins and forming large, dense cluster; stem leaves fewer and shorter, with enlarged bases; inflorescence dense terminal raceme; perianth cream-white; pedicels long, slender; stamens exserted; capsule broadly ovate.

Frequent, often abundant, in open woods. Lower H and C. Frog Camp; Lake Valley; Benson-Tenas Lakes 1585-1645 m (5200-5400 ft); Spring L.

14. IRIDACEAE   Iris Family

Perenial herbs; leaves narrow, 2-ranked; perianth parts 6; ovary inferior.

SISYRINCHIUM L.

Sisyrinchium idahoense Bick. Bull. Torrey Club 26:445. 1899. IDAHO BLUE-EYED GRASS. Simple usually leafless stems 20-35 cm high; leaves half as long as the stems, 1.5-3 mm wide, glabrous; perianth purple, about 1 cm long; ovary puberulent; capsule globose.

Very rare, observed only on moist grassy border of Craig L. 1555 m (5100 ft). Probably brought in by stock. Usually found growing in moist grassy places, C and AT.

15. ORCHIDACEAE   Orchid Family

Perennial herbs with corms, bulbs, tuberous roots or rootstocks; flowers irregular, perianth superior, 3 sepals and 3 petals; stamens united with the style; ovary inferior forming a one-celled capsule; seeds minute, numerous.

KEY TO THE GENERA OF ORCHIDACEAE

Plants without green leaves...*Corallorhiza*
Plants with green leaves
  Leaves all basal, white-veined...*Goodyera*
Leaves not all basal
  Lip spurred...*Habenaria*
  Lip spurless, flowers twisted spirally in spike...*Spiranthes*

CORALLORPHIZA R. Br.

Corallorhiza trifida Chatelain, Spec. Inaug. 8. 1760. EARLY CORAL-ROOT. Slender scape 10-15 cm high; leaves reduced to a few sheathing bracts; raceme usually short, 5-10-flowered; bracts minute; flowers purplish; capsule oblong about 10 mm long.

Rare in woods. Lower H (C and T). West Lava Camp 1535 m (5036 ft).

Corallorhiza maculata Raf. Am. Month. Mag. 2:119. 1817. SPOTTED CORAL-ROOT. Stout scape 25-50 cm high, purplish with 3 sheathing scales; raceme of 15-30 flowers; bracts minute; pedicels 2 mm long; flowers brownish purple, 7 mm long; lip white, spotted with dark red; capsule oblong 7-13 mm long.

Rare in area. Woods, Sims Butte. H to T.

GOODYERA R. Br.

Goodyera decipiens (Hook.) St. John and Const. Fl. SE Wash. 99. 1937. (*Goodyera oblongifolia* Raf.). RATTLESNAKE PLANTAIN. Stout scape 15-30 cm high, glandular-pubescent; leaves all basal, 3-7 cm long, narrowly ovate, veins often irregularly bordered with white especially the midvein, petioles broad; spike 6.5-13 cm long, many-flowered, somewhat one-sided; flowers greenish-white; upper sepals united with the petals into a galea; petals about 8 mm long.

Occasional in woods. Lower H to T. Tenas Lakes 1645 m (5400 ft); Sims Butte at 1585 m (5200 ft); West Lava Camp.

HABENARIA Willd.

Herbs with fleshy fibrous roots; flowers small, white or greenish in terminal spikes.

KEY TO THE SPECIES OF HABENARIA

Perianth white, spur not saccate..*H. leucostachys*

Perianth greenish, spur saccate..*H. saccata*

Habenaria leucostachys (Lindl.) Wats. Bot. Calif. 2:134. 1880. WHITE-FLOWERED BOG ORCHID. Roots tuberous, elongated; stem stout 20-40 cm high; leaves lanceolate, reduced upward; spike densely flowered, 6.5-20 cm long; flowers white, fragrant, about 13 mm long; spur about as long, very slender.

Occasional in marshy places. H to T. Upper Squaw Cr. 1830 m (6000 ft); Three Cr. Meadow 1920 m (6300 ft); Park Meadow 1875 m (6150 ft).

Habenaria saccata Greene, Erythea 3:49. 1895. (*H. gracilis* Wats.). SLENDER BOG ORCHID. Stem 30-60 cm high; leaves oblanceolate to lanceolate, somewhat smaller upward; spike many-flowered, to 30 cm long; flowers under 13 mm long, greenish or purplish; lip obtuse, twice as long as the very saccate spur.

Frequent in marshy places. H to T. Frog Camp; Sparks Lake area.

SPIRANTHES L. C. Rich

Spiranthes romanzoffiana Cham. & Schl. Linnaea 3:32. 1828. HOODED LADIES' TRESSES. Roots tuberous; stem stout, glabrous, 15-30 cm high; leaves linear to lanceolate, 5-13 cm long, the upper reduced to bracts; flowers dense in a twisted spike, white, about 7 mm long; lip oblong, constricted below the dilated apex.

Occasional in moist meadows. H to T. Scott L.; Three Creek L.

16. SALICACEAE   Willow Family

Shrubs or trees; leaves simple, alternate, with stipules, deciduous; dioecious, flowers in catkins (aments), each flower subtended by a bract.

KEY TO THE GENERA OF SALICACEAE

Leaves broad, long-petioled; bud scales numerous..*Populus*

Leaves narrow, short-petioled; bud scales one..*Salix*

POPULUS L.

Populus trichocarpa T. & G. Hook. Icon. Pl. 9: pl. 878. 1852. BLACK COTTONWOOD. At lower elevations it grows to large size but in this area is much dwarfed. Height about 7.6 m (25 ft). Bark gray; leaves 8-12 cm long, ovate or narrower, acute, finely crenate-serrate, glabrous, shining above, much paler beneath; petioles 5 cm long; catkins about 10 cm long; capsules pubescent; seeds with long coma.

Rare. Lower H. Frequent along streams in C and HT. Pole Bridge; Pine Butte.

SALIX L. Willow

Dioecious shrubs with slender branches; alternate, narrow leaves with stipules; flowers in catkins; stamens 1 or 2, sometimes more; capsule 2-valved.

KEY TO THE SPECIES OF SALIX

Capsules glabrous or nearly so (sometimes hairy is *S. commutata*)
    Style 0.8-1.8 mm long; leaves more densely hairy above than
        beneath, the under side soon glabrous, shiny, reticulate...........................*S. barclayi*

    Style 0.5-1 mm long; leaves more densely hairy beneath than
        above or about equally hairy on both sides or becoming
        glabrous...*S. commutata* & var.

Capsules hairy (see also *S. commutata*)
    Styles obsolete or very short, stamens 2
        Scales black, ovate, long hairy; leaves variable, mostly
            broadly oblanceolate to obovate; satiny to rusty-
            pubescent to glaucous beneath.....................................*S. scouleriana*

        Scales light brown, narrowly oblong, thinly hairy;
            leaves narrowly lanceolate-elliptic, acute,
            becoming glabrous above, glaucous
            and rusty-pubescent beneath...................................*S. geyeriana* var. *meleina*

    Styles 0.5-1.5 mm long; stamens 1 or 2
        Stamens 1; capsule satiny-pubescent; leaves dull
            green above, dense silvery, appressed,
            short-hairy beneath...*S. sitchensis*

        Stamens 2; capsule grayish with dense wooly hairs;
            leaves tomentose on both sides..*S. eastwoodiae*

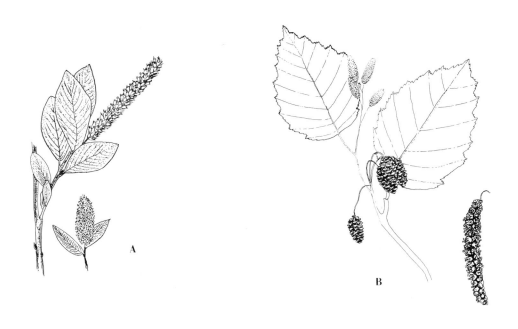

A *Salix commutata*; **B** *Alnus sinuata*

Salix barclayi Anderss. Oefvers. Svensk. Vet. Akad. Foerhandl. 15:125. 1858. (Nord.Am. Pil.). BARCLAY'S WILLOW. Slender shrub 1-2.5 m high; new twigs dark brown or blackish, glabrous or with scattered hairs; leaves 2-6 cm long, 1-2.5 cm wide, elliptic to obovate, acute or obtuse, base cuneate or rounded, margins entire or glandular-serrete; both surfaces long-hairy when young, the lower soon becoming glabrous, shining, reticulate, the upper side green, becoming thinly hairy to glabrate, the midrib more persistently hairy; stipules small, leaf-like; catkins on short leafy peduncles; scales brown or blackish, persistent, long-hairy; staminate catkins up to 3 cm long; stamens 2, filaments glabrous; pistillate catkins 2.5-5 cm long; capsule 4-6 mm long, glabrous; pedicel short, mostly less than 1.5 mm long; style 0.8-1.8 mm long, longer than the short bilobed stigmas.

Occasional near lakes and streams. H. Sparks L.; Todd L.; Three Creek L.

Salix commutata Bebb, Bot. Gaz. 13:110. 1888. VARIABLE WILLOW. Shrub 1-2.5 m high; twigs brown to blackish, quite hairy to glabrous; leaf-blades 4-7 cm long, 1.2-5 cm wide, elliptic, narrowly ovate to oblanceolate, acute, cuspidate, base tapered to rounded, entire or glandular-serrulate; both leaf-surfaces densely or loosely tomentose when young, especially beneath, becoming thinly pubescent to glabrate in age, not paler or glaucous beneath; petioles short, stout, hairy; stipules leaf-like, up to 1 cm long; catkins appearing with the leaves on short leafy peduncels; scales obtuse, brownish, long-hairy, persistent; stamens 2, filaments glabrous; pistillate catkins 3-6 cm long when mature; capsule glabrous or sparsely to densely short-hairy, 3-6 mm long, on short pedicel up to 1.5 mm long; style 0.5-1 mm long; stigma shorter, more or less bilobed.

Common near lakes and streams. H. McKenzie Pass area; Lake Valley; White Branch Cr.; Sparks L.; Park Meadow 1875 m (6150 ft).

Var. *denudata* Bebb. Young leaves glabrous or nearly so, more distinctly serrulate. With the species.

Var. *puberula* Bebb. Capsule thinly to densely pubescent. With the species.

Salix eastwoodiae Cockerell, in Heller, Cat. N. Am. Pl. ed. 2, 89. 1910. EASTWOOD'S WILLOW. Low shrub, 0.5-1 m high; branches stout; twigs dark brown, pubescent; leaves elliptic-lanceolate, 3-7 cm long, 1-2.5 cm wide, mostly entire, grayish tomentose both surfaces, thinly so with age; catkins on leafy peduncles, the staminate about 2 cm long, pistillate twice as long; scales broadly lanceolate, tomentose, brown; stamens 2; filaments hairy as base; capsule 4-6 mm long, grayish with wooly hairs.

Infrequent in wet ground. H. Green Lakes 2000 m (6550 ft).

Salix geyeriana Anderss, var. **meleina** Henry, Fl. So. Brit. Columbia, 98. 1915. GEYER WIILOW. Shrub, 1-2 m high; branches slender, very leafy; leaves 2.5-5 cm long, 5-10 mm wide, elliptic to linear-oblanceolate, acuminate, margins entire, thinly pubescent above becoming glabrate, rusty villous and glaucous beneath; catkins on leafy peduncles, the staminate 1 cm long; pistillate often longer; scales narrowly oblong, light yellowish, red-tipped; stamens 2; filaments hairy lower half; style obsolete; stigma divided; capsule 4-5 mm long, short hairy.

Occasional in wet places. H and C. Scott L.; Trout Cr. Swamp; Three Creek L. area at 1970 m (6450 ft).

Salix scouleriana Barr. in Hooker, Fl. Bor. Am. 2:145. 1839. SCOULER WILLOW. Shrub to 4.5 m high; leaves mostly oblanceolate to obovate, obtuse, 2.5-6 cm long, entire or shallowly toothed; young leaves hairy, more densely so beneath than above; mature leaves dark green and glabrous above, glaucous and sparsely reddish-strigillose beneath varying to somewhat puberulent above to densely villous beneath; stipules small; catkins appear before leaves; scales blackish, persistent, long-hairy; capsules narrow, long-beaked, densely short-hairy, 5-8 mm long; style shorter than the stigmas; stamens 2, filaments glabrous.

Occasional in wet or dry places. Lower H to C. Trout Cr. Swamp; Windy Point; Sand Hills; Matthieu L. 1860 m (6100 ft); West Lava Camp.

Salix sitchensis Sanson, in Bongard, Mem. Acad. Imp. Sci. St. Petersb. VI. 2:162. 1833. SITKA WILLOW. Shrub to 4 m high; twigs dark, usually glabrous; leaves 4-6 cm long, 1.5-2 cm wide, oblanceolate or broadly so, entire, dull green and thinly pubescent with impressed veins, eventually glabrate above; gray with a dense shiny pubescence beneath; catkins on short leafy-bracted peduncles, the staminate 2-4 cm long, pistillate up to 6 cm long; scales brown, long-hairy, usually much darker on the staminate catkin; stamens 1, filaments glabrous; capsules densely short-hairy, 3-5.5 mm long; pedicel short, less than 1 mm long; style 0.5-0.8 mm long.

Infrequent near streams. H to T. West Lava area; Soda Creek Tr.

17. BETULACEAE Birch Family

Shrubs or trees, leaves alternate, flowers monoecious, in aments, the staminate drooping, the pistillate erect or drooping and in spike-like clusters or capitate.

KEY TO THE GENERA OF BETULACEAE

Pistillate aments in a receme; scales thick, persistent..*Alnus*

Pistillate aments solitary; scales thin, deciduous..*Betula*

ALNUS Hill Alder

Leaves deciduous, dentate or serrate; staminate aments (catkins) long and drooping; pistillate erect, becoming woody when mature, forming a cone.

KEY TO THE SPECIES OF ALNUS

Leaves shining; peduncles slender, mostly longer than the cones.....................*A. sinuata*

Leaves dull; peduncles stout, mostly shorter than the cones...........................*A. tenuifolia*

Alnus sinuata (Regel) Rydb. Bull. Torrey Club 24:190. 1897. SITKA ALDER. A shrub, usually large; bark gray; leaves ovate 5-9 cm long, acute apex, rounded base, sharply and doubly serrate, glabrous above, lighter and resinous beneath; staminate catkins with large ovate scales; cones 1-2 cm long on slender peduncles usually longer.

Infrequent along streams and lakes. H to T. Melakwa L.; Benson L.; Soda Cr. at 1740 m (5700 ft).

Alnus tenuifolia Nutt. Sylva 1:32. 1842. MOUNTAIN ALDER. Shrub 1-2 m high; bark smooth gray-brown; leaves ovate, apex acute, base rounded, 5-9 cm long, mostly glabrous above, pubescent on veins beneath, doubly serrate; pistillate cones on short, stout peduncles.

Infrequent along streams. AT and C. Trout Cr. Swamp.

BETULA L. Birch

Betula glandulosa Michx. Fl. Bor. Am. 2:180. 1803. SCRUB BIRCH. Shrub 90-120 cm high, slender branched; twigs dotted with resinous glands; leaves broadly ovate to orbicular, 1.2-2 cm long, crenate-dentate, glabrous, paler and reticulate beneath; petioles 3-6 mm long; pistillate cones 1.3-2 cm long, about 3 mm thick.

Occasional on east side in wet meadows. H to C. Three Cr.; Park Meadow 1875 m (6150 ft).

18. FAGACEAE   Beech Family

CASTANOPSIS Spach.

Trees or shrubs; leaves evergreen, alternate, simple; flowers monoecious, borne in aments; staminate flowers many, in clusters of 3 in the axils of bracts; pistillate flowers 1-3 subtended by an involucre; ovary 3-celled; styles 3, fruit of 1-3 ovoid nuts enclosed in the spiny involucre.

Castanopsis crysophylla (Dougl.) A. DC. Seem. Journ. Bot. 1:182. 1863. CHINQUAPIN. A small tree in this area 3-7.5 m (10-25 ft) high; bark thick; leaves lanceolate 6.5-9 cm long, on short petioles, tapering at the ends, thick, leathery, yellow tomentose beneath; burs very prickly.

Infrequent in dry open woods. Lower H to HT. Tenas Lakes; Sims Butte; Black Crater at 1525 m (5000 ft).

19. SANTALACEAE   Sandalwood Family

Mostly plants of tropical regions.

COMANDRA Nutt.

Perennial herbs, stems erect, woody base; leaves alternate, entire; calyx companulate, 5-lobed, the tube lined with a 5-lobed disk; stamens 5, opposite the calyx-lobes; anthers attached to the calyx-lobes by tuft of fine hairs; petals none; fruit 1-seeded, nut-like.

Comandra umbellata (L.) Nutt. Gen. 1:157. 1818. BASTARD TOAD-FLAX. Stems slender, branched, 15-30 cm high; leaves sessile, elliptic, 12-20 mm long, 3-6 mm wide; flowers several, short pediceled, red-tinged-white; drupe globose.

Infrequent in dry open woods. Lower H to T. Pine Butte; Tenas Lakes; Trout Cr. Butte area.

20. LORANTHACEAE   Mistletoe Family

Evergreen plants parasitic on trees or shrubs; dichotomously branched; leaves opposite, thick, leathery; flowers dioecious, petals none; ovary inferior; fruit a berry; seeds with a glutinous coating.

ARCEUTHOBIUM Marsch.-Bieb.

Parasitic on coniferous trees. Plants yellowish, fragile; leaves scale-like.

KEY TO THE SPECIES OF ARCEUTHOBIUM

Staminate flowers in spikes, parasitic on *Abies* ....*A. abietinum*

Staminate flowers paniculate, parasitic on *Pinus contorta* ....*A. americanum*

Arceuthobium abietinum Engelm. Proc. Am. Acad. 8:401. 1872, nomen nudum. FIR DWARF MISTLETOE. Stems 5-7.5 cm long, greenish-brown, much branched; staminate flowers numerous; fruit a berry 3-4 mm long.

Rare in this area, growing on the branches of *Abies grandis*. C and AT. Trout Cr. Butte.

Arceuthobium americanum Nutt. Engelm. Bost. Journ. Nat. Hist. 6:214. 1850. AMERICAN DWARF MISTLETOE. Staminate plant 2 cm or more long, the pistillate much shorter. Fruit a small, bluish, glaucous berry.

Infrequent, growing on trunk and branches of *Pinus contorta murrayana*. H and C. McKenzie Pass area; Three Cr. area.

21. POLYGONACEAE   Buckwheat Family

Herbs or shrubs with jointed stems; leaves alternate, opposite or whorled, simple, entire, often with sheathing stipules; flowers mostly perfect; calyx 3-6-lobed or -parted; petals none; stamens 3-9; pistil 1, ovule 1; stigmas 2-3; fruit a 3-angled achene.

KEY TO THE GENERA OF POLYGONACEAE

Calyx 5-parted ....*Polygonum*

Calyx not 5-parted
   Sepals 4; stigmas 2; leaves reniform ....*Oxyria*

   Sepals 6; stigmas 3; leaves not reniform
      Flowers enclosed in involucre ....*Eriogonum*

      Flowers not enclosed in involucre ....*Rumex*

A *Comandra umbellata;* **B** *Polygonum newberryn;* **C** *Oxyria digyna*

ERIOGONUM Michx.

Annual or perennial herbs or near shrubs; leaves entire, alternate or whorled, exstipulate, petiolate, often tomentose; flowers in clusters, which are subtended by a 4-8-lobed involucre, these grouped variously; calyx 6-cleft, petaloid; stamens 9; pistil 1, ovary 1-celled; styles 3; fruit a 3-angled achene.

KEY TO THE SPECIES OF ERIOGONUM

Calyx pubescent, whitish to rose-colored ....*E. pyrolaefolium* var.

Calyx glabrous, yellow ....*E. umbellatum*

Eriogonum pyrolaefolium Hook. var. **coryphaeum** T. & G. Proc. Amer. Acad. 8:162. 1870. AL-PINE ERIOGONUM. Caudex stout, woody; leaves ovate-oval, 12-36 mm long, glabrous above, densely white or brownish tomentose beneath; flowering stem 6.5-12 cm high, usually tomentose; umbel of 3 short rays and subtended by 2 narrow bracts; involucres turbinate, one with each ray; calyx white, pink tinged, about 3 mm long.

Common in open sandy places. H. Pine Butte 1645 m (5400 ft); Sims Butte 1720 m (5635 ft); Middle Sister, west side at 2135 m (700 ft); Ball Butte.

Eriogonum umbellatum Torr. Ann. Lyc. N. Y. 2:241. 1828. SULFUR-FLOWERED ERIOGONUM. Plant loose-matted, lower stems branched, woody, leafy at tips; leaves ovate to broadly elliptic, white tomentose beneath, light brown thinly tomentose above, 6-18 mm long with petioles usually longer; flowering stem 5-30 cm high, floccose; umbel simple subtended by leafy bracts; rays 2-6 variable in length; involucre tomentose; 10-20 flowered, the outer reflexed; calyx yellow or tinged with red.

Common in dry open places. H to T. Lake Valley; South and Middle Sister to about timberline; Green Lakes; Ball Butte.

OXYRIA Hill

Oxyria digyna (L.) Hill. Hort. Kew. 158. 1768. MOUNTAIN SORREL. Caudex thick, branching; stems many, 5-15 cm high; leaves reniform, 15-25 mm broad, glabrous, mostly basal; petioles long, slender; racemes dense, narrow; pedicels very slender; sepals reddish-green; achenes flat, 5 mm broad including the wide membranous wings.

Frequent above timberline. A. Middle Sister, west side at 2380 m (7800 ft); South Sister at 2440 m (8000 ft).

POLYGONUM L. Knotweed

Annual or perennial herbs; leaves alternate, entire; stipules united forming scarious sheath.

KEY TO THE SPECIES OF POLYGONUM

Inflorescence a single spike-like terminal raceme ....*P. bistortoides*

Inflorescence not a single terminal raceme
  Perennial, leaves large, oval; rootstock thick, woody ....*P. newberryi*

  Annual, leaves smaller, elliptic or narrow;
    rootstock not thick, woody
    Leaf-blades jointed on the petioles
      Fruit reflexed on curved pedicels ....*P. douglasii*

      Fruit erect on pedicels
        Flowers in small clusters in most of the leaf axils,
          leaves ovate to obovate ....*P. minimum*

        Flowers crowded in terminal clusters, sometimes in
          lower leaf axils; bracts linear; leaves few, linear ....*P. kelloggii*

    Leaf-blades not jointed on the petioles, linear-lanceolate;
      sheaths deeply cut into numerous slender whitish
      divisions, obscuring the flowers ....*P. parryi*

Polygonum bistortoides Pursh Fl. Amer. Sept. 271. 1814. MOUNTAIN MEADOW KNOTWEED. Rootstock fleshy; stems glabrous, 30-60 cm high; basal leaves oblong, narrow, glabrous, 9-13 cm long on petioles as long; stem leaves smaller, sessile; inflorescence solitary 1.5-2.5 cm long, thick-cylindric, dense; flowers on slender pedicels, calyx about 3 mm long, 5-lobed, white; stamens exserted; achenes dark brown, 3-angled, smooth.

Infrequent in moist meadows. H and C. Green Lakes 2000 m (6550 ft) ; Mesa Cr.

Polygonum douglasii Greene, Bull. Calif. Acad. 1:125. 1885. DOUGLAS KNOTWEED. Annual, slender, sometimes branched, 12-30 cm high; leaves lanceolate, sessile, 15-30 mm long, 3-8 mm wide, revolute; flowers 1-3 in axils, reflexed; calyx greenish-white with red mid-veins; stamens 8; achenes 3-angled, black, shining.

Occasional in dry rocky ground. H to T. West Lava Camp; Frog Camp; North Sister; Todd L.

Polygonum kelloggii Green, Fl. Fran. 134. 1891. KELLOGG'S KNOTWEED. Annual, slender, simple or branched from the base, glabrous, 2.5-5 cm high; leaves linear about 12 mm long; inflorescence a leafy-bracted spike; bracts green; flowers usually rose-pink, 1.5 mm long; achenes brown, smooth.

Rare in meadows. H and C. Hand L.

Polygonum minimum Wats. Bot. King Expl. 315. 1871. LEAFY KNOTWEED. Annual, slender, simple or branched from the base, 2.5-7.5 cm high; leaves numerous, ovate, somewhat scurfy, 1-15 mm long, nearly sessile; flowers 2-3 in the leaf axils; calyx lobes green with white or pinkish margins; achenes black, shining.

Rare in rocky places. H to C. Upper Soda Cr.; Todd L.

Polygonum newberryi Small, Bull. Torrey Club. 21:170. 1894. NEWBERRY'S KNOTWEED. Perennial, stems several, spreading, 15-30 cm high, from fleshy rootstock; leaves ovate 3.8-6 cm long, appressed-hairy beneath, glabrate above; racemes few-flowered; calyx pinkish-green; achenes brown, shining.

Comon in sandy volcanic soil. A and H. Frog Camp; Scott Mt.; Sunshine Shelter; Three Creek L.

Polygonum parryi Greene, Bull. Torrey Club. 8:99. 1881. PRICKLY KNOTWEED. Annual, low, glabrous, freely branched; leaves crowded, narrow; flowers single, sessile, in most leaf axils, pinkish; achenes 3-angled, dark brown, shining.

Reported only from Lake Valley, collected by E. P. Sheldon No. 12590. 13 mm high. This specimen was not seen.

RUMEX L.

Rumex acetosella L. Sp. Pl. 338. 1753. SHEEP SORREL. Perennial herb, usually simple, glabrous, 15-30 cm high; leaves narrowly hastate, 2.5-5 cm long, the lower long-petioled; dioecious; panicle narrow, many-flowered; flowers minute; the staminate greenish to red, stamens 6, exserted, filaments short; styles 3; achenes granular.

Occasional, up to timberline. Introduced in the U. S., a native of Europe.

22. CHENOPODIACEAE   Goosefoot Family

CHENOPODIUM L.

Chenopodium album L. Sp. Pl. 219. 1753. PIGWEED. Annual herb, usually branched, about 25 cm or less high. At lower elevations in fields and cultivated ground it may grow to 2 m in height. Herbage mealy, stem grooved; leaves long ovate, irregularly toothed; inflorescence terminal and in leaf axils, the clusters mealy; calyx-lobes loosely enclosing the utricle; seeds black.

An introduced weed, native of Europe. Probably brought into this area in horse feed. West Lava Camp. Rare and apparently not spreading.

23. PORTULACACEAE   Purslane Family

Annual or perennial herbs, somewhat succulent; leaves alternate or opposite, simple, entire; sepals usually 2, unequal; petals mostly 5; stamens often 5, opposite the petals; ovary mostly superior, 1-celled; styles and stigmas 2-8; fruit a capsule.

KEY TO THE GENERA OF PORTULACACEAE

Flowers in a dense umbel ....*Spraguea*
Flowers not in a dense umbel
  Capsule 3-valved, dehiscing from the apex
    Plants with fleshy taproots ....*Claytonia*
    Plants with fibrous roots ....*Montia*
  Capsule circumscissile ....*Lewisia*

CLAYTONIA L.

Claytonia bellidifolia Rydb. N. Amer. Fl. 21:301. 1932. RYDBERG'S CLAYTONIA. SPRING BEAUTY. Perennial with large fleshy taproot and thick, often branching caudex; leaves crowded at base, fleshy, obovate, on long petioles; inflorescence few-flowered; petals white to pink, about 6 mm long; stamens 5; capsule ovate.

Infrequent on loose rocky slopes. A and upper H. North Sister; South Sister at 2745 m (9000 ft).

LEWISIA Pursh

Succulent, glabrous perennial from a corm or fleshy root; stem leaves few; sepals 2, stamens 5-many; style 1; stigmas 3-8; capsule 1-celled.

KEY TO THE SPECIES OF LEWISIA

Fleshy taproot; leaves several, basal ....*L. pygmaea* var.

Globose corm, leaves 2-3, cauline ....*L. triphylla*

Lewisia pygmaea (Gray) Robinson var, **aridorum** Bartlett, Bot. Gaz. 44:303. 1907. ALPINE LEWISIA. Plant less than 2.5 cm high; taproot fleshy, often branched; stems several, with gland-tipped bracts above the middle; basal leaves linear with broad bases, longer than the stems; 2-3-flowered; sepals about 4.5 mm long, toothed, gland-tipped, the glands dark red; petals 6-8, white or pink, longer than the sepals, toothed and gland-tipped at the apex; stamens 5-8; seeds many, minute, shining.

Rare. H. Dry mountain meadow in coarse sandy soil near Todd L. 2075 m (6800 ft).

Lewisia triphylla (Wats.) Robinson in A. Gray Syn. Fl. N. Amer. 1:269. 1897. THREE-LEAVED LEWISIA. Perennial from deep-seated corm; stems 1 or more about 2.5 cm high; leaves 2, opposite, linear, 2-5 cm long; basal leaves soon disappearing; flowers mostly 2-4, pink; petals 5 or more, about 5 mm long; stamens 5; seeds many, minute, shining.

Infrequent in meadows. H. Scott L.; Huckleberry L. 1585 m (5200 ft).

MONTIA L. Miner's Lettuce

Stem leaves 2, free ....*M. cordifolia*

Stem leaves 2, united ....*M. perfoliata*

Montia cordifolia (Wats.) Pax. & Hoffm, in Engler & Prantl, Nat. Pflanzenf. ed. 2.1c:259. 1934. CORDATE-LEAVED MONTIA. Perennial, 10-30 cm high; slender creeping rootstock; basal leaves several, sub-orbicular, 2.5-5 cm long on long petioles; stem leaves 2, sessile; raceme few flowered; petals 5, white, about 1 cm long; fruit a capsule; seeds 3, black, shining.

Rare on moist banks of streams. H to C. Mesa Cr. 1740 m (5700 ft).

Montia perfoliata Howell var. **depressa** (Gray) Jepson Fl. Calif. 471. 1914. SMALL MINER'S LETTUCE. Succulent annual, glabrous, low, spreading, often reddish, stems several, 4-7.5 cm high; 2 stem-leaves below the inflorescence united, forming an orbicular disk, basal leaves several, deltoid to rhombic, petioled; flowers pinkish, numerous in a short raceme; petals 5 with notched apex, about 2 mm long; seeds 3, black.

Rare in moist open places. Lower H to T. McKenzie Pass area.

SPRAGUEA Torr.

Spraguea umbellata Torr. var. **caudicifera** Gray, Syn. Fl. N. Amer. 1:278. 1897. PUSSY PAWS. Low spreading perennial; caudex branching; taproot long, woody; basal leaves numerous, fleshy, spatulate, glabrous, 1-3 cm long; flowering stems 3-6 cm high with few small leaves; glomerate-capitate inflorescence; flowers white or red-tinged; sepals about 6 mm long, very broad, scarious.

Common in dry sandy soil. A and H. Pine Butte; Lake Valley; North, Middle and South Sister above timberline; Three Creek L.

24. CARYOPHYLLACEAE   Pink Family

Annual or perennial herbs; stems nodose with opposite, entire leaves; flowers regular, usually perfect; sepals 4-5 separate or united into a tube; petals 4-5 or wanting, often lobed; stamens usually twice the number of petals; styles 2-5; ovary superior, 1-celled; fruit a capsule; seeds many, small.

KEY TO THE GENERA OF CARYOPHYLLACEAE

Sepals distinct, flowers small
  Stipules wanting
    Petals two-cleft ....*Stellaria*
  Petals entire
    Styles as many as the sepals and alternate with them ....*Sagina*
    Styles fewer than the sepals ....*Arenaria*
  Stipules present ....*Spergularia*
Sepals united forming a 5-toothed tube ....*Silene*

ARENARIA L.

Leaves mostly basal, narrowly linear, curved ....*A. formosa*
Leaves not basal; narrowly elliptic to lanceolate ....*A. macrophylla*

Arenaria formosa Fischer. ex DC. Prod. 1:402. 1824. MOUNTAIN SANDWORT. Cespitose perennial from woody base; fertile shoots 7.5-15 cm or more high, glandular; sterile shoots much shorter; basal leaves very narrow, 2.5-5 cm long; stem-leaves few, shorter; inflorescence a few-flowered cyme; sepals broad, obtuse, about 3 mm long; petals twice as long, 5, white; capsule longer than the sepals.

Rare in rocky soil. H. West of South Sister 1525-1830 m (5000-6000 ft).

Arenaria macrophylla Hook. Fl. Bor. Amer. 1:102. pl. 37. 1830. LARGE-LEAVED SANDWORT. Perennial with slender creeping rootstocks forming loose mats; stems branched, 5-10 cm high, short-pubescent; leaves acute, 1.5-2.5 cm long; flowers few on long peduncles; sepals acute, about 3.5 mm long; petals little longer, 5, white; capsule short.

Rare in dry open woods. Lower H to T. Black Crater, north base at 1525 m (5000 ft).

SAGINA L.

Sagina occidentalis Wats. Proc. Amer. Acad. 10:344. 1875. WESTERN SANDWORT. Low annual, matted, glabrous, 2.5-3.8 cm high; leaves linear, acute; flowers minute, few on each stem, long pediceled; petals 5, white, shorter than the sepals; capsule longer than the sepals.

Occasional in moist places. H to T. Frog Camp; Lake Valley; Trout Cr. Swamp 1355 m (4450 ft); Sparks L.; Green Lakes 2000 m (6550 ft).

SILENE L.

Leaves very few, opposite, widely separated; petals 6-cleft ....*S. oregana*
Leaves many, crowded at base; petals 2-lobed ....*S. suksdorfii*

Silene oregana Wats. Proc. Amer. Acad. 10:343. 1875. OREGON CAMPION. Perennial herb, short-pubescent, glandular above; stems several from branching rootstock, 30 cm high; leaves narrowly lanceolate,, entire, 3.5-5 cm long; inflorescence a several-flowered cyme; calyx cylindric, 10-nerved, lobes short acute, very glandular, about 1.2 cm long; petals 5, white, longer than the calyx, cleft into narrow segments; capsule oblong.

Rare in dry, rocky slopes. H. Soda Cr. at 1725 m (5650 ft).

Silene suksdorfii Robins. Bot. Gaz. 16:44. 1891. SUKSDORF'S CAMPION. Perennial, tufted, 6-9 cm high, densely glandular above; leaves many, mostly basal, linear-spatulate, 1-2.5 cm long, puberulent; flowers 1-5 on each stem; calyx 12 mm long, narrowly-campanulate, with about 10 distinct purple veins, lobes short, obtuse; petals 5, white, notched, little longer than the calyx; capsule ovoid.

Occasional in rocky places. A. Ball Butte, summit; Broken Top above 2440 m (8000 ft); North, South and Middle Sister, above timberline; Little Brother.

SPERGULARIA Pers.

Spergularia rubra (L.) J. & C. Presl, Fl. Cech. 94. 1819. SAND SPURRY. Annual or perennial; prostrate, stems 2.5-7.5 cm long, branched from base forming mat, glandular above; leaves linear, 3-6 mm long, clustered; stipules large; flowers single in leaf-axils, long-pediceled; sepals glandular, ovate, scarious-margined, 3 mm long; petals 5, pink-purple, shorter than the sepals; capsule acute.

Rare in this area. Introduced, native of Europe. West Lava Camp.

STELLARIA L.

Perennial herbs, slender, mostly glabrous; flowers cymose, some in leaf-axils; sepals 5; petals 5, white, 2-cleft; stamens not more than 10; styles 3, rarely 4-5; ovary 1-celled, many-ovuled; capsule mostly ovoid, dehiscent by twice as many valves as styles.

KEY TO THE SPECIES OF STELLARIA

Flowers not umbellate, petals present
    Bracts of the inflorescence green, foliaceous;
        petals shorter than the sepals ....*S. borealis* & var.
    Bracts of the inflorescence scarious; flowers few,
        terminal; petals longer than the sepals ....*S. longipes*
Flowers in umbellate cymes, petals none ....*S. umbellata*

Stellaria borealis Bigelow, Fl. Bost. ed. 2. 182. 1824. NORTHERN STARWORT. Perennial, pubescent; stems weak, 5-25 cm high; leaves ovate-elliptic, 6-20 mm long, sessile, thin, little reduced upward; inflorescence leafy, cymose; pedicels long, slender; sepals glabrous with scarious margin, 2-3.5 mm long; petals white, 2-lobed, shorter than the sepals; capsule longer than the calyx.

Occasional in moist places. H. Green Lakes; Todd L.; Park Meadow 1875 m (6150 ft).

S. borealis Bigelow var. **bongardiana** Fernald, Rhodora 16:151. 1914. Glabrous, to 30 cm high; leaves lanceolate, entire, 2.5-3.8 cm long, reduced upward; sepals 4.5 mm long or less, acute.

Infrequent in moist places. C to T. Found mostly at lower altitudes. Trout Cr. Swamp 1355 m (4450 ft).

Stellaria longipes Goldie, Edinb. Phil. Journ. 6:327. 1822. LONG-STALKED STARWORT. Perennial, stems slender, glabrous, often branched, tufted, 10-20 cm high; leaves linear-lanceolate, sessile, about 2.5 cm long; flowers few, terminal; pedicels long, slender, erect; bracts scarious; sepals thin, acute, scarious-margined, 3-4.5 mm long; petals white, 2-cleft, longer than the sepals; stamens 10; capsule about as long as the calyx or longer.

Infrequent in wet meadows. H to T. Near Three Creek L. 1965 m (6450 ft).

Stellaria umbellata Turcz. Bull. Soc. Nat. Mosc. 15:173. 1842. UMBELLATE CHICKWEED. Glabrous herb; stems 7.5-20 cm long, slender, weak, often branched; leaves sessile, long-ovate, 6-12 mm long; internodes 2-3 times as long; terminal flowers in umbellate cymes, the lower axillary; pedicels long, slender, with a pair of small scarious bracts; sepals 2-3 mm long, acute, scarious-margined; petals none; capsule longer than the sepals.

Rare in dry open woods. H to C. Todd L.

25. NYMPHAECEAE   Water Lily Family

Perennial aquatic herbs, acaulescent; flowers axillary, solitary; sepals 5-7; petals 5 to many; stamens 5 to many, hypogynous; carpels compound, superior; stigmas united, fruit indehiscent, dry, many-seeded.

Nymphaea polysepala (Engelm.) Greene, Bull. Torr. Club. 15:84. 1888. WESTERN YELLOW POND-LILY. Rootstock thick, cylindric; leaves floating, deeply cordate, 13 cm or more long; sepals 6 or more, 4-5 cm long, thick, yellow; petals many, narrow, reddish at base, partially hidden by the many reddish stamens; fruit ovoid, seeds many.

Infrequent in lakes and ponds. H to T. Tenas Lakes 1645 m (5400 ft); Sparks L.

26. RANUNCULACEAE   Buttercup Family

Annual or perennial herbs; leaves simple or compound; flowers hypogynous; sepals distinct; petals distinct or wanting; stamens numerous; carpels distinct few to many.

KEY TO THE GENERA OF RANUNCULACEAE

Carpels several seeded, in fruit follicles or berries
  Flowers regular
    Leaves simple, cordate-orbicular ....*Caltha*

    Leaves compound
      Sepals spurred, fruit a cluster of distinct follicles ....*Aquilegia*
      Sepals not spurred, fruit a berry ....*Actaea*

  Flowers irregular
    Upper sepal hood-like enclosing the 2 petals ....*Aconitum*
      Upper sepal spurred; petals 4, the upper pair enclosed
        by the spurred sepal ....*Delphinium*

Carpels 1-seeded, in fruit achenes
  Cauline leaves 3 in a whorl, sepals pealoid, petals none ....*Anemone*

  Culine leaves alternate, sepals not petaloid, petals present ....*Ranunculus*

ACONITUM L.

Aconitum columbianum L. var. **Howellii** (Nels. & Macbr.) C. L. Hitchc. Vas. Pl. Pac. N. W. Pt. 2:321. 1964. HOWELL'S ACONITE. MONKSHOOD. Perennial; stems 75-100 cm high, weak, ascending, pubescent to glandular above; leaves petiolate, palmately 3-5 parted or deeply cleft, the divisions lobed or cleft; inflorescence simple, few-flowered, often flowers entirely replaced by bulblets in the axils; flowers helmet-shaped, blue; fruit usually 3 follicles, slightly pubescent, many-seeded. This variety differs little from the species.

Infrequent in moist shaded places. H to AT. Soda Springs 1770 m (5800 ft).

ACTAEA L.

Actaea arguta Nutt. ex. Torr. & Gray, Fl. N. Amer. 1:35. 1838. WESTERN BANEBERRY. Perennial, 30-75 cm high; stout rootstock; stem puberulent, bracnhed; leaves few, large, ternately compound, the leaflets lobed and toothed; racemes short, dense; petals 4-10, small; stamens numerous, longer than the petals; fruit a red berry; seeds several, in two rows.

Infrequent in damp woods. H to HT. West Lava Camp; Soda Cr.

ANEMONE L.

Perennial herbs; leaves basal, palmately compound or divided; usually 2-3 reduced leaves forming an involucre on the stem; sepals 5 or more, petal-like; petals none; stamens many; carpels numerous, 1-seeded; in fruit forming a head of achenes.

A *Silene suksdorfii;* **B** *Anemone occidentalis*

KEY TO THE SPECIES OF ANEMONE

Styles much elongated and plumose ....*A. occidentalis*

Styles not elongated or plumose
  Achenes densely long-hairy
    Styles slender, leaflet segments linear ....*A. drummondii*

    Styles stout, leaflet segments oblong ....*A. multifida*

  Achenes densely short pubescent ....*A. lyallii*

Anemone drummondii S. Wats. Bot. Calif. 2:424. 1880. DRUMMOND'S ANEMONE. Perennial; rootstocks stout, clustered; stems slender, 10-25 cm high, villous; basal leaves long-petioled, long-hairy, about 3-ternately compound; flower solitary; sepals 5 or more, 1-2 cm long, inner surface white, outer bluish-purple, hairy; heads globose, 1 cm broad; styles slender, persistent; achenes densely woolly.

Occasional in sandy places. H. Pine Butte; Black Crater 2215 m (7260 ft); South Sister 2590 m (8500 ft); Ball Butte.

Anemone lyallii Britt. Ann. N.Y. Acad. 6:227. 1891. (*A. quinquefolia* var. *Lyallii* (Britt.) Robinson in A. Gray, Syn. Fl. N. Amer. 1¹:13. 1895.). LITTLE MOUNTAIN ANEMONE. Perennial herb; rootstocks horizontal, light-colored; stems 7.5-18 cm high, slender, thinly pubescent above; cauline leaves 3 in a whorl forming an involucre, ternately compound, the leaflets 1.3-4 cm long, narrowly obovate, lobed or serrate, the margins ciliate; flower solitary on long peduncle; sepals 5, white or light purple, 1 cm or less long, elliptic; stamens 15-35; carpels many; achenes densely pubescent, short-beaked.

Frequent in open woods. H to T. Lake Valley; McKenzie Pass.

Anemone multifida Poir. var. **globosa** Torr. & Gray, Fl. N. Amer. 1:13. 1838. GLOBOSE ANEMONE. Perennial; rootstocks stout; stems hairy, 5-25 cm high, sometimes branched; basal leaves long-petioled, sparsely villous, 2-3 times ternately parted, the segments oblong, acute, to 2.5 cm long; sepals oval, yellow or purple-tinged, about 1 cm long; head globose; achenes densely villous.

Rare in open woods. H. Broken Top.

Anemone occidentalis Wats. Proc. Amer. Acad. 11:121. 1876. MOUNTAIN PASQUE FLOWER. Stout woody rootstocks; stems scapose, clustered, 30-45 cm high when mature, ¼ as high at flowering time, villous; basal leaves long-petioled, ternate, the divisions bi-pinnately divided and lobed forming acute linear segments, villous; involucral leaves sessile; flowers solitary; sepals 6-8 or more, petal-like, oval, about 2.5 cm long, villous and bluish tinged without, glabrous and white within; achenes villous, reflexed, numerous, forming a head, the styles developing into long plumose tails.

Occasional in mountain meadows and open woods. H. Skyline Tr. west of Middle Sister; Black Crater; Sunshine Shelter.

AQUILEGIA L.

Perennial herbs; leaves mostly basal, ternately decompound; flowers showy, terminating the branches; sepals 5, petal-like; petals 5, each spurred at the base; stamens numerous, the inner becoming staminodia; carpels 5 developing into follicles.

Aquilegia formosa Fisch. DC. Prod. 1:50. 1824. WESTERN COLUMBINE. Stout rootstock; stem glabrous below, 30-60 cm high; leaves mostly basal, long-petioled, ternately compound, the leaflets about 2 cm long, cleft and lobed, glabrous above, pale beneath; flowers nodding, about 2.5 cm or more long, the sepals and spurs scarlet, the petal blades yellow; fruits, 5 slender pubescent follicles about 2.5 cm long.

Infrequent in moist open woods. H to T. Sand Hills; Scott Mt.; Soda Springs 1770 m (5800 ft).

CALTHA L.

Perennial herbs, fleshy, with mostly basal leaves; sepals large petal-like, deciduous; petals none; stamens numerous; carpels several; fruit follicles.

KEY TO THE SPECIES OF CALTHA

Leaves broader than long, reniform, basal lobes overlapping ....*C. biflora*

Leaves longer than broad, cordate, basal lobes not overlapping ....*C. leptosepala*

Caltha biflora DC. Syst. 1:310. 1818. WHITE MARSH-MARIGOLD. Perennial, succulent, glabrous; 15-37.5 cm high, rarely branched; leaves basal, long petioled, reniform 5-7.5 cm broad, undulate, the basal sinus deep; stems 1- rarely 2-flowered; sepals 8-12, white, narrow-oblong, 1-2 cm long; follicles short stipitate.

Occasional in marshy places. H. Pole Bridge; Skyline Tr. west of Middle Sister.

Caltha leptosepala DC. Syst. 1:310. 1818. SLENDER-SEPALED MARSH-MARIGOLD. Perennial, succulent, glabrous; stems 15-30 cm high; leaves basal, 3.8-6.5 cm long, long-petioled, cordate base, oblong-ovate, longer than broad, crenate; scape 1-2 flowered; sepals 8-12, white, oblong, 1-2 cm long; follicles nearly sessile.

Occasional in marshy ground, sometimes with C. biflora. H. Pole Bridge-Scott L. area; Sparks L.; Three Creek L.

DELPHINIUM L.

Perennial herbs; stems simple or branched; leaves palmately lobed or divided, the segments tipped with a whitish nodule; sepals 5, petal-like the upper forming a basal spur; petals 4, the upper 2 forming a spur enclosed within the calyx spur; carpels 3, forming follicles; seeds many.

KEY TO THE SPECIES OF DELPHINIUM

Mature follicles 8-12 mm long, the tips only spreading; seeds
with whitish wings on the lateral angles ....*D. depauperatum*

Mature follicles 12-15 mm long, widely recurving; seeds with
very narrow wings or none on the lateral angles ....*D. menziesii* var.

Delphinium depauperatum Nutt. in Torr. & Gray, Fl. N. Amer. 1:33. 1838. DWARF LARKSPUR. Clustered, fleshy, tuberous roots; stem slender, erect, 30-60 cm high, usually glabrous below, glandular-pubescent above; leaves few, basal or nearly so, long petiolate; the few cauline leaves reduced, bract-like, lobes linear; sepals blue, 9-15 mm long, often glandular, the spur long, slender; petals bluish-white; follicles nearly erect, the tips spreading, glandular-villous.

Infrequent in open woods and meadows. H. Headwaters of Linton Cr., 1830 m (6000 ft).

Delphinium menziesii DC. var. **pyramidale** (Ewan) C. L. Hitchc. Vas. Pl. Pac. NW. pt. 2:255. 1964. MENZIES' LARKSPUR. Tubers thick, irregular; stems usually simple, 30-60 cm high, glabrous to pubescent; basal leaves long-petioled, 2.5-6 cm broad, 3-5 parted, the segments cuneate, 3-lobed or more, the lobes oblong; raceme open, 5-20-flowered, the lower long pediceled; e spals dark purple, ovate, 12-25 mm long; spur as long or longer than the sepals; petals whitish with purple veins; anthers many, blue; follicles about 15 mm long, divergent, long-beaked, pubescent.

Frequent in open woods and meadows. H to T. Lake Valley; headwaters of Linton Cr. 1830 m (6000 ft); Green Lakes; Three Cr.; Todd L.

RANUNCULUS L.

Perennial herbs, erect or procumbent; sepals 5; petals usually 5, yellow or white, with nectary at base; stamens 10 or more; carpels many forming a head.

KEY TO THE SPECIES OF RANUNCULUS

Aquatic plants; submerged leaves finely dissected; petals white
with yellow base; seeds with transverse ridges ....*R. aquatilis* var.

Terrestrial plants; leaves never dissected; petals yellow;
seeds not transversely ridged
Leaves entire or slightly lobed
Stems decumbent; basal leaves ovate to orbicular
on long slender petioles ....*R. gormanii*

Stems erect; basal leaves lanceolate, narrowed to slender
petioles 2-3 times longer than the blades ....*R. alismaefolius* var.

Leaves 3-parted, the center lobe entire,
the 2 lateral segments lobed ....*R. eschscholtzii*

Ranunculus alismaefolius Geyer var. **alismellus** A. Gray. Proc. Amer. Acad. 7:327. 1868. PLANTAIN-LEAVED BUTTERCUP. Perennial, tufted, 15-40 cm high, slightly pubescent; leaves mostly basal, broadly lanceolate, the blades 2.5-5 cm long tapering to petioles 2-3 times as long; stem leaves smaller and narrower; flowers 1-3; sepals 5, shorter than the petals, thinly pubescent on outer surface; petals 5, about 7 mm long, obovate, yellow, the inner surface glossy; achenes many forming a head, beak short curved.

Frequent in wet meadows and lake borders. H to C. Lake Valley; Green Lakes; Skyline Tr. west of Middle Sister.

Ranunculus aquatilis L. var. **capillaceus** (Thuill.) DC. Prod. 1:26. 1824. WATER BUTTERCUP. Perennial, glabrous, 30 cm or more long; stems submerged, rooting at the nodes; leaves all submerged, about 2.5 cm long, somewhat broader, petiolate, divided into numerous filiform segments; flowers floating, few on long pedicels; sepals deciduous, shorter than the petals; petals 5, white with yellow base, about 6 mm long; stamens 10 or more; achenes 20 or more in cluster, each short beaked.

Rare in lakes and sluggish streams. H. Found mostly at lower elevations, T and US. Todd L., outlet 1860 m (6100 ft).

Ranunculus eschscholtzii Schlecht, Animad. Ranunc. 2:16 pl. 1. 1820. ESCHSCHOLTZ'S BUTTERCUP.

Short caudex; stems few, in cluster, little branched, glabrous, 15-30 cm high; leaves 1.5-2.5 cm long, and broader, 3-parted, the 2 lateral lobes again lobed, the center one entire, the lobes oblong, obtuse, glabrous; basal leaves long-petioled, the upper cauline sessile; sepals purple-tinged, shorter than the petals, hairy; petals 5, about 6.5 mm long, yellow; achenes many forming elongated head.

Occasional in grassy places near timberline. A and H. Sunsihne Shelter 2045 m (6700 ft); South Sister; Black Crater 1980 m (6500 ft).

Ranunculus gormanii Greene. Pittonia 3:91. 1896. GORMAN'S BUTTERCUP. Roots fusiform, clustered, light-colored; stems 10-20 cm high, slender, decumbent, sometimes rooting at the nodes; leaves ovate 12.5-25 cm long on villous petioles; flowers usually solitary, terminal, on long peduncles; sepals ovate, glabrous; petals 5, yellow, obovate, about 6.5 mm long; achenes few forming small head.

Frequent in wet meadows. H. Frog Camp; Lake Valley.

27. BERBERIDACEAE   Barberry Family

Herbs or shrubs; leaves alternate or basal, simple or compound; sepals and petals distinct, usually in 3's, or wanting; stamens as many as the petals and opposite them; anthers opening by 2 valves; carpel 1, 1-celled.

KEY TO THE GENERA OF BERBERIDACEAE

Perennial herbs with a single basal leaf, 3-foliate, large ....*Achlys*

Low shrubs, leaves pinnate, the teeth spine-tipped ....*Berberis*

ACHLYS DC

Achlys triphylla (Smith) DC. Syst. 2:35. 1821. VANILLA-LEAF. Plant glabrous; single leaf basal, long-petioled, the blade orbicular in outline, about 15 cm broad; leaflets 3, large, broadly fan-shaped, sinuate-lobed; scape slender, about 30 cm high; flowers small, forming dense spike; calyx and corolla wanting; stamens 8-12; ovary ovoid; stigma sessile; fruit a follicle, reniform, somewhat fleshy, becoming dry, indehiscent, 1-seeded.

Rare in woods. Lower H. Frequent in HT. Spring L. 1555 m (5100 ft).

BERBERIS L.

Shrubs, the wood of stems and roots yellow; compound spiny leaves; flowers yellow, racemose, terminal; sepals and petals in series; stamens hypogynous, opposite the petals; fruit a berry.

Berberis nervosa Pursh, Fl. Amer. Sept. 1:219. pl. 5. 1814. (*Mahonia nervosa* Nutt.). LOW OREGON GRAPE. Small low shrub, 15-30 cm high; leaves pinnately compound. 11-15 leaflets which are obliquely long-ovate, spiny-serrate; racemes few, elongated; berries 8 mm in diameter, glaucous, blue, on short pedicels.

Rare in H. Common in HT. Pine Butte 1645 m (5400 ft).

28. FUMARIACEAE   Fumitory Family

DICENTRA Bernh.

Delicate perennial herbs, glabrous, with watery juice; leaves dissected, basal or cauline; flowers flattened, heart-shaped, in recemes or panicles, capsule oblong or linear.

Dicentra formosa (Andr.) Walp. Rep. 1:118. 1842. PACIFIC BLEEDING HEART. Creeping rootstock; scape slender, 20-40 cm high; leaves basal, long-petioled, ternately decompound, the divisions cleft and lobed, glaucous beneath, 15 cm or more broad; panicle several-flowered; corolla purplish-pink, cordate, about 2 cm long, the spurs short, rounded, incurved; capsules 2 cm long; seeds black, shining.

Occasional in open woods. H to HT. Lava Camp L. 1585 m (5200 ft); Sunshine Shelter; North Sister near timberline; Soda Cr. 1740 m (5700 ft).

29. CRUCIFERAE   Mustard Family

Herbs with acrid juice; leaves alternate, simple or compound; flowers usually racemose; sepals 4; petals 4, mostly clawed; stamens usually 6, tetradynamous; pistil 1, of 2 united carpels, superior; fruit a silique or silicle.

KEY TO THE GENERA OF CRUCIFERAE

Length of pods 4 or more times the width
  Siliques terete or slightly 4-sided
    Pods terete, curved; seeds ovoid, 2 rows in each cell ....*Rorippa*

    Pods slightly 4-angled, straight, seeds flattened,
      1 row in each cell ....*Barbarea*

  Siliques flattened or slightly so
    Pods lanceolate to elliptic-lanceolate, under 2 cm long
      Leaves pinnately-parted, canescent; valves keeled ....*Smelowskia*

      Leaves simple, valves not keeled ....*Draba*

    Pods not lanceolate; elongated, oblong, ovate
      Valves of pods nerveless; 2-celled, one row of seeds in each ....*Cardamine*

      Valves nerved at least below the middle, seeds in 1 or 2 rows
        Pods linear ....*Arabis*

        Pods oblong ....*Draba*

Length of pods less than 4 times the width
  Pods compressed at right angles to the septum, cuneate ....*Capsella*

  Pods compressed parallel to the septum ....*Draba*

ARABIS L.

Annual or perennial herbs; entire or dentate leaves; petals white or purplish; siliques linear, compressed parallel to the septum, valves 1-nerved, dehiscent; seeds flattened, usually winged, in one or two rows in each cell.

KEY TO THE SPECIES OF ARABIS

Pods erect or ascending
  Pods 1-2.5 mm wide
    Seeds in 1 row, orbicular, winged all around
      Plant stellate-pubescent, 30-90 cm high ....*A. divaricarpa*

      Plant glabrous, less than 30 cm high ....*A. lyallii*

    Seeds in 2 rows, broadly elliptical,
      winged on sides and lower end ....*A. drummondii*

  Pods 4-5 mm wide ....*A. platysperma*

Pods reflexed or spreading ....*A. holboellii*

A *Berberis nervosa;* **B** *Arabis lyallii;* **C** *Cardamine bellidifolia pachyphylla;*
D *Drapa aureola*

Arabis divaricarpa A. Nels. Bot. Gaz. 30:193. 1900. SPREADING-POD ROCK CRESS. Biennial, 30-70 cm high; stems 1-few, erect, slender, stellate below, glabrous above; basal and lower leaves petioled, lanceolate to oblanceolate, mostly entire, acute, stellate; the upper narrower, auriculate, glabrous; racemes elongated; sepals half as long as the petals; petals pinkish, 6-8 mm long; siliques spreading, 5-7.5 cm long, about 1.5 mm broad, pediceled.

Rare on gravelly banks. H to mostly AT. Soda Cr. at Sparks L. 1665 m (5460 ft).

Arabis drummondii Gray var. **interposita** (Greene) Rollins Res. Stud. State Coll. Wash. 4:45. 1936. DRUMMOND'S ROCK CRESS. Biennial or perennial, 30 cm or more high, stellate-pubescent to glabrous above; stems one or more from base; basal leaves oblanceolate, entire, pubescent, 2 cm or more long; stem leaves narrowly-oblong, sessile, auriculate; flowers small, white to purplish; pods mostly erect, crowded, about 5 cm long, 1.5 mm wide.

Infrequent on rocky slopes. H. Obsidian Cliffs 1890 m (6200 ft).

Arabis holboellii Hornem. var. **secunda** (How.) Jeps. Man. Fl. Pl. Calif. 430. 1925. SECUND ROCK CRESS. Biennial or perennial; stems mostly single, simple, 30 cm or higher, densely stellate below to glabrous above; leaves oblanceolate, mostly entire, densely pubescent, 2-3 cm long; stem leaves sessile, auriculate, lanceolate, stellate; sepals stellate, purplish, 3 mm long; petals white to rose-purple, about 6.5 mm long; pods 4 cm or more long, very narrow; seeds in 1 row in each 2 cells.

Frequent in NE sector. AT and C. Trout Cr. Butte 1680 m (5500 ft).

Arabis lyallii Wats. Proc. Amer. Acad. 11:122. 1876. LYALL'S ROCK CRESS. Perennial, 4-20 cm high; stems several from woody base, glabrous; basal leaves many, glabrous except base of petioles, narrowly-spatulate, mostly entire, 1.2-1.8 cm long; stem leaves with or without auricles; petals 4, pink, 4.5-8 mm long; pods erect, 2.8-5 cm long, about 2 mm broad.

Frequent in timberline area. A and H. Scott Mt. 1830 m (6000 ft); Little Brother at 2290 m (7500 ft); South Sister.

Arabis platysperma Gray, Proc. Amer. Acad. 6:519. 1865. BROAD-SEEDED ROCK CRESS. Perennial; stems several, 7.5-22.5 cm high, glabrous and glaucous or stellate-pubescent; basal leaves narrowly-oblanceolate, entire, stellate or glabrous; stem leaves sessile; petals few, white to reddish-purple, 4.5-6.5 mm long; pods erect, 3.8-5.8 cm long, about 4.5 mm broad; seeds large, orbicular, with broad encircling wing.

Frequent. H. Black Crater; Obsidian Cliffs; North Sister; Green Lakes; Wickiup Plain 1920 m (6300 ft).

BARBAREA R. Br.

Biennial herbs, glabrous; stems angled; flowers small, yellow; siliques elongated, slightly 4-angled, sessile, valves ribbed; seeds 1 row in each cell, flat without margin.

Barbarea americana Rydb. Mem. N. Y. Bot. Gard. 1:174. 1900. WINTER CRESS. Biennial, 15-45 cm or more high, often purplish; lower leaves lyrate, 3.8-10 cm long, the terminal division large; flowers in dense racemes; petals yellow; pods ascending, 2.5-4 cm long about 1.5 mm wide, beaked.

Infrequent, moist stream-banks. H to T. Frog Camp; Soda Cr.

CAPSELLA Medic.

Capsella bursa-pastoris (L.) Medic. Pflanzeng. 1:85. 1792. SHEPHERD'S PURSE. Annual, usually not over 15 cm high; stellate-pubescent; basal leaves lanceolate, about 3.8 cm long, dentate to lobed; stem leaves smaller, auriculate; raceme elongated at maturity; flowers tiny, white; pedicels longer than the fruit; silicles broadly wedge-shaped with persistent style at apex; seeds many.

Infrequent in this area. A wide spread naturalized weed from Europe. West Lava Camp.

CARDAMINE L.

Cardamine bellidifolia L. var. **pachyphylla** Cov. in Proc. Biol. Soc. Wash. 11:170. 1897. ALPINE BITTER-CRESS. Perennial, glabrous, 5-7.5 cm high; fleshy branched caudex; leaves fleshy, ovate to round, slightly lobed, 6-12 mm long on long petioles; corymbs few-flowered; petals white or purplish, 4.5 mm long; pods 2-3.2 cm long, about 1 mm wide; seeds in 1 row in each cell.

Frequent in rocky places. A and H. North and Middle Sister; Black Crater; Green Lakes.

DRABA L.

Low herbaceous plants, mostly stellate-pubescent; leaves simple, mostly entire; flowers small, in racemes; petals yellow or white, entire; stigma entire; pods oblong or linear, flattened parallel to the septum; seeds in 2 rows in each 2 cells.

KEY TO THE SPECIES OF DRABA

Perennial, stems leafy, densely so below
    raceme short many flowered, pods oblong ....*D. aureola*

Annual, stem leaves few, mainly basal,
    raceme elongated not densely flowered, pods linear-oblong ....*D. stenoloba*

Draba aureola Wats., Bot. Calif. 2:430. 1880.
GREAT ALPINE WHITLOW-GRASS. Plant stellate-pubescent, 5-12 cm high; stem usually branched; leaves crowded below the inflorescence, oblanceolate, obtuse, 12-25 mm long, stem leaves smaller; flowers in a compact raceme; petals yellow; sepals glabrous; pods oblong, broad, stellate-pubescent, 6.5-12 mm long; style about 1.5 mm long.

Common above timberline in loose volcanic sand and rocks. A. On all three Sisters up to 3050 m (10,000 ft).

Draba stenoloba Ledeb., Fl. Ross. 1:154. 1841.
SLENDER WHITLOW-GRASS. Slender annual, simple or branched from the base, 15-30 cm high; leaves mostly in a basal tuft, about 2.5 cm long, oblanceolate to elliptical, glabrate above, thinly stellate beneath; flowers minute, petals yellow; pods narrow, slightly curved, about 1 cm long.

Infrequent in damp grassy places. H. Green Lakes Tr.; Soda Cr. at Sparks L.

RORIPPA Scop.

Aquatic or marsh annuals or perennials, glabrous, branching; leaves simple or pinnately lobed; flowers minute, yellow, in racemes; style stout; pods terete; seeds minute, 2 rows in each cell.

Rorippa curvisiliqua (Hook.) Bessey, Mem. Torrey Club. 5:169. 1894. WESTERN YELLOW-CRESS. Annual or biennial, branching, 15-45 cm high; leaves 2.5 cm or more long, variously pinnately lobed; pods curved, about 1 cm long.

Infrequent, wet sandy shores. Lower H and below. Hand L. 1465 m (4800 ft); Sparks L.

SMELOWSKIA C. A. Mey

Low matted perennials; densely stellate-pubescent; leaves pinnatifid; flowers small, racemose; petals white or tinged, obovate; style short, pods slightly compressed.

Smelowskia ovalis Jones, Proc. Calif. Acad. IV. 5:624. 1895. ALPINE SMELOWSKIA. Stems 7.5-15 cm high, from woody caudex; leaves pinnately compound, the parts deeply lobed; flowers small, light purplish; pods ovoid to narrowly oblong, rounded at base, about 4.5 mm long; seeds few.

Infrequent in timberline areas. A and H. Little Brother 2290 m (7500 ft); North Sister.

Leptarrhena amplexifolia

30. CRASSULACEAE   Stonecrop Family

GORMANIA Britt.

Perennial, fleshy, succulent, glabrous herbs; flowers in terminal cymes; calyx 5-lobed; petals 5 united below the middle; stamens 10, borne on the corolla-tube; carpels 5, erect, united below.

Gormania watsonii Britt. Bull. N.Y. Bot. Gard. 3:29. 1903. WATSON'S GORMANIA. Rootstocks horizontal, stout, branching; basal leaves fleshy, crowded, spatulate, rounded, about 2.5 cm long, glaucous, sometimes reddish-tinged; stem leaves smaller, alternate; panicle many-flowered; petals united at base, about 7 mm long, light yellow, oblong, obtuse; anthers pinkish.

Occasional on rocky bluffs and slopes. H. Benson-Tenas Lakes 1615 m (5300 ft); Wickiup Plain; upper Soda Cr. area.

31. SAXIFRAGACEAE   Saxifrage Family

Perennial herbs; leaves alternate or basal, exstipulate; calyx 5-lobed, the tube free or adnate to the ovary; petals 5 distinct, alternating with the calyx-lobes, rarely absent; stamens equaling or twice as many as the calyx-lobes, usually borne on the calyx-tube; pistil of 2 or 3 carpels, mostly united, rarely distinct; ovary 1 or 2-celled, superior or partly inferior; fruit a capsule or follicle.

KEY TO THE GENERA OF SAXIFRAGACEAE

Staminodia present, alternating with the 5 anthers;
    scapose; flower solitary..*Parnassia*

Staminodia none; plant scapose or caulescent; flowers several
  Placentae axial; ovary 2-celled
    Carpels almost distinct, fruit a pair of follicles................................*Leptarrhena*

    Carpels more or less united, fruit a capsule, or follicles.....................*Saxifraga*

  Placentae parietal or nearly basal; ovary 1-celled
    Petals entire or wanting
      Capsule membranous...*Tiarella*

      Capsule not membranous..*Heuchera*

    Petals not entire...*Mitella*

HEUCHERA L.

Perennial herbs; rootstocks stout, scaly; leaves mostly basal, long-petioled, palmately-veined; inflorescence paniculate; calyx-tube companulate, adnate to lower half of ovary; calyx 5-lobed; petals 5, white, entire; stamens 5 opposite the sepals; styles 2; capsules opening between the 2 spreading beaks.

Heuchera glabra Willd. ex Roem. & Sch. Syst. Veg. 6:216. 1820. ALPINE HEUCHERA. Stems about 30 cm high, glabrous below, leafless or with 1 or 2 small leaves; basal leaves several, ovate in outline, cordate base, doubly and acutely lobed, 2.5-7.5 cm long, on petioles twice as long; panicle open, glandular; calyx-lobes minute, broad; petals spatulate, long-clawed, about 2 mm long; stamens exserted.

Infrequent on rocky cliffs. H. Little Bro.; Sunshine Shelter.

LEPTARRHENA R. Br.

Perennial herbs; leaves leathery, mostl ybasal; flowers small, in a dense panicle; petals 5, white, entire; stamens 10, filaments broadened toward base; the 2 carpels joined at base only; fruit a pair of follicles.

Leptarrhena amplexifolia (Sternb.) Ser. in DC. Prod. 4:48. 1830. FALSE SAXIFRAGE. Caudex horizontal, scaly; plant about 30 cm high; basal leaves 5-7.5 cm long, oblong, serrate except basal part, glabrous, dark green above, pale beneath; petioles winged; 1-2 stem leaves smaller, clasping; petals about 2 mm long; follicles 8 mm long, reddish-purple, the tips slightly spreading; seeds numerous, long, narrow, the outer coat extending on both ends.

Rare along wooded streams. H. West Lava Camp; Spring L.

MITELLA L.

Leaves mostly basal; flowers small in racemes; calyx-tube short, the lower part adnate to the ovary; petals white or green, deeply pinnately cleft; stamens 5, very short; capsule 1-celled with 2 almost basal placentae, several seeded; seeds smooth.

KEY TO THE SPECIES OF MITELLA

Stamens opposite the sepals
    Leaves reniform to round-cordate, glabrate..*M. breweri*

    Leaves ovate to oval with cordate base, hirsute..*M. ovalis*

Stamens opposite the petals..*M. pentandra*

Mitella breweri Gray, Proc. Amer. Acad. 6:533. 1865. BREWER'S MITREWORT. Flowering stem 15-25 cm high; leaves 3-7.5 cm broad, serrate-crenate, glabrous except hairy veins beneath, long petioled; raceme long, slender; flowers green, about 4.5 mm broad on short pedicels; calyx-lobes broad; petals pinnately divided, the few divisions filiform; stamens opposite the sepals; stagmas 2-lobed.

Frequent in moist woods. H and C. Lake Valley; Scott Mt.; Sunshine Shelter; Wickiup Plain.

Mitella ovalis Greene, Pittonia 1:32. 1887. OVAL-LEAVED MITREWORT. Plant 20-30 cm high; leaves shallowly lobed, the lobes crenate, 2.5-3.8 cm long, scattered slightly curved hairs; petioles long; flowers small in slender raceme, green; pedicels short; petals pinnately-divided, the divisions few, filiform; stamens opposite the sepals.

Rare in moist woods. Lower H. Occurs mostly in

HT. West Lava Camp.

Mitella pentandra Hook. Bot. Mag. 56: pl. 2933. 1829. FIVE-POINT MITREWORT. 20-40 cm high; leaves basal, broadly cordate, 2.5-5 cm long, shallowly lobed, coarsely crenate, scattered hairs, petioles long; raceme slender; flowers small, green, on short pedicels; petals pinnately divided into few irregular divisions; stamens opposite the petals.

Frequent in moist woods. H and C. Lake Valley; Sparks L.; Green Lakes; Three Creek L.

PARNASSIA L.

Herbs, scapose, glabrous; leaves basal (often one sessile on scape), entire, petioled; flowers solitary, terminal, white; calyx 5-lobed; petals 5, each with a cluster of gland-tipped sterile stamens at the base; stamens 5, opposite the sepals; stigmas 4, sessile; capsule 1-celled; seeds numerous, winged.

KEY TO THE SPECIES OF PARNASSIA

Staminodial scales with 3 short thick lobes..*P. fimbriata*

Staminodial scales with 6-12 slender gland-tipped filaments..*P. intermedia*

Parnassia fimbriata Konig, Ann. Bot. 1:391. 1804. FRINGED GRASS-OF-PARNASSUS. Scape about 30 cm high; basal leaves long-petioled, reniform, 2.5-3.5 cm broad; small clasping single bract slightly above the middle of the scape; sepals about 5 mm long; petals obovate, about 10 mm long, short-clawed, fimbriate on the lateral margins; clusters of sterile filaments fleshy, short, thick-lobed, not gland-tipped.

Rare on wet banks of streams. H and C. Soda Springs.

Parnassia intermedia Rydb. N. Amer. Fl. 22:78. 1905. CASCADE GRASS-OF-PARNASSUS. Scape 10-22.5

cm high; basal leaves broadly-ovate, 1.5-2.5 cm broad, long-petioled; small sessile bract well below the single flower; sepals elliptic, about 5 mm long; petals elliptic, about 10 mm long, lower lateral margins sparsely lacerate; several sterile filaments united below in clusters, slender and gland-tipped above.

Rare along streams in wet meadows. H and C. Todd L. 1860 m (6100 ft).

SAXIFRAGA L.

Perennial herbs; leaves mostly basal, without stipules; flowers perfect, in panicles, usually small; calyx 5-lobed; petals 5; stamens 10, perigynous; carpels 2.

KEY TO THE SPECIES OF SAXIFRAGA

Leaves mostly basal, not fleshy
    Leaves orbicular in outline..*S. arguta*

Leaves not orbicular, longer than broad
    Flowers slightly irregular, pedicels long, filiform..*S. ferruginea*

    Flowers regular, pedicels not long, filiform..*S. oregana*

Leaves not basal; crowded on stems, fleshy..*S. tolmiei*

Saxifraga arguta D. Don. Trans. Linn. Soc. 13:356. 1822. MT. MEADOW SAXIFRAGE. Slender herb; rootstock long; scape 25-50 cm high; leaves basal, long-petioled, reniform to slightly orbicular, coarsely dentate, 2.5-5 cm broad; inflorescence glandular, glabrous below, spreading, flowers relatively few; calyx-lobes oblong, slender, reflexed; petals white with 2 yellow spots near base, orbicular, clawed, about 3 mm long; filaments broadened upward; anthers purple; the 2 carpels united part way up, about 8 mm long.

Infrequent on stream banks. H. Linton Cr., springs 1860 m (6100 ft); Soda Springs area.

Saxifraga ferruginea Graham, Edinb. Nem Phil. Jour. 1828:349. 1829. RUSTY SAXIFRAGE. Stems branched, 20-35 cm high; leaves mostly basal, spatulate, 2.5-7:5 cm long, broadly toothed above the middle, pubescent; inflorescence open, spreading, glandular-pubescent; calyx lobes reflexed, shorter than the petals; petals unequal, long clawed, white and some with 2 yellow spots, about 4.5 mm long; stamens 10, filaments slender; capsules about 4.5 mm long, the two carpels united upward to the middle.

Infrequent along streams. H. Scott L.; Sunshine Shelter; Obsidian Falls 1980 m (6500 ft).

Saxifraga oregana How. Erythea 3:34. 1895. OREGON SAXIFRAGE. Rootstocks stout; scapes stout, fistulose, 30-75 cm high, glandular-pubescent; leaves 5-15 cm long, ovate, oblong to spatulate, remotely serrate, lower half ciliate, narrowed to broad base; flowers dense on few branches; calyx-lobes ovate, reflexed, about 2.5 mm long; petals white, broadly ovate, about 4 mm long, short-clawed; filaments shorter than the petals; capsule about 4 mm long with 2 short spreading beaks.

Occasional in marshy meadows and along streams. H. to HT. Frog Camp; Spring L.; Fall Cr.; Linton Cr.

Saxifraga tolmiei T. & G. Fl. N. Amer. 1:537. 1840. TOLMIE'S SAXIFRAGE. Low tufted perennial, much branched, creeping, w o o d y b e l o w; leaves crowded; thick, sessile, glabrous, oblong, 6-10 mm long; flower-stalk erect, slender, 5-10 cm high, gland-ular-pubescent, leafless or with 1-2 reduced leaves; flowers few; calyx-lobes broadly ovate, glabrous, 3 mm long or less; petals white, mostly spatulate, about 4 mm long; filaments clavate; capsules about 1 cm long, mottled with purple, the 2 beaks widely divergent.

Occasional on high rocky slopes. A and upper H. Black Crater; Broken Top; North, Middle and South Sister.

TIARELLA L.

Perennial herbs; leaves mostly basal, long-petioled, lobed or trifoliate; panicle simple; flowers small; sepals 5; petals 5, white; stamens 10, long exserted on slender filaments; styles elongated; carpels 2 united; capsules 1-celled with very unequal valves.

Tiarella unifoliata Hook. Fl. Bor. Amer. 1:238. 1832. WESTERN COOLWORT. Stems 20-40 cm high, 1-several from a scaly rootstock, glandular-pubescent above; leaves cordate in outline, 2.5-6 cm broad, 3-5-lobed, crenate-dentate, on petioles 5-12.5 cm long, the cauline leaves on shorter petioles; panicle narrow; sepals white or pink-tinged, about 2 mm long; petals longer, linear; stamens about 4 mm long; capsule of 2 unequal carpels, one half as long as the other.

Rare in the area. C. Common in woods at lower elevations. Trout Cr. Swamp 1355 m (4550 ft).

32. GROSSULARICEAE   Gooseberry Family

Shrubs, prickly or smooth; leaves alternate, palmately-veined, usually lobed; flowers perfect, regular; ovary inferior, the calyx-tube adnate to it below; calyx 5-lobed, usually more showy than the petals, persistent; petals 5 inserted on the calyx-tube; stamens 5, alternate with the petals and inserted near the top of the calyx-tube.

RIBES L.

Ovary 1-celled with parietal placentae, fruit a several-seeded berry.

KEY TO THE SPECIES OF RIBES

Plants with spines or prickles..R. lacustre
Plants without spines or prickles
  Calyx saucer-shaped, ovary with sessile glands.................................R. petiolare
Calyx not saucer-shaped, ovary with stalked glands or none
  Leaves with stalked glands, pedicels about equaling
    the bracts, berries black..R. viscosissimum var.
  Leaves without stalked glands, pedicels much shorter
    than the bracts, berries red..R. cereum

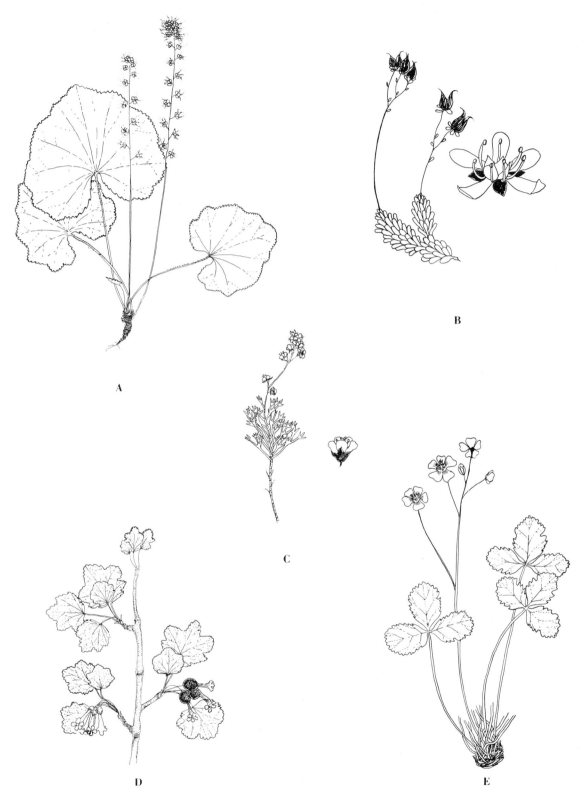

A *Mitella breweri*; B *Saxifraga tolmiei*; C *Luetkea pectinata*; D *Ribes cereum*;
E *Pontilla flabellifolia*

Ribes cereum Dougl. Trans. Hort. Soc. Lond. 7:512. 1830. SQUAW CURRANT. Much branched shrub, 0.5-1.5 m high; leaves broader than long, 1.5-4 cm broad, 3-5-lobed, the lobes crenate or dentate, glandular-pubescent, petioles about equaling the blades; calyx white or pinkish, the lobes short, reflexed; petals 5, very small, inserted near the top of the calyx-tube opposite the calyx-lobes; stamens alternate with the petals; berry about 8 mm in diameter, glabrous, red.

Occasional in dry open woods. H and C. Pine Butte; Black Crater 2135 m (7000 ft); Pole Bridge; Obsidian Cliffs.

Ribes lacustre (Pers.) Poir. in Lam. Encycl. Suppl. 2:56. 1812. PRICKLY CURRANT. Shrub 1 m high, more or less decumbent; 3 or more spines at the internodes, many smaller ones on the branches; leaves somewhat cordate in outline, deeply 3-5-lobed, the lobes incised or lobed, thin, glabrous, lighter beneath, the blades 2.5-5 cm long on long slender petioles; racemes 10-15 flowered; flowers green, purplish within; calyx saucer-shaped, the sepals broad, short; petals broad, short; stamens 5, short; berry black, 6-9 mm in diameter, with long gland-tipped hairs.

Infrequent along streams and in moist meadows. Lower H and C. West Lava Camp; White Branch Cr.

Ribes petiolare Dougl. Trans. Hort. Soc. Lond. 7:514. 1830. WESTERN BLACK CURRANT. Shrub 1 m or more high, mostly erect; leaves 5-lobed, the lobes dentate, the blade 6-12 cm wide, thin, glabrous except resinous-dotted beneath, petioles long, slender; racemes about 10 cm long, erect, many-flowered; pedicels slender, much longer than the tiny bracts; calyx-tube deep bowl-shaped, resinous-dotted; calyx-lobes white, about 5 mm long; berry about 6 mm in diameter, black, resinous-dotted.

Rare in the area, moist stream banks. AT. Trout Cr. Swamp.

Ribes viscosissimum Persh. var. **hallii** Jancz. Mem. Soc. Geneve. 35:328. 1907. STICKY CURRANT. Shrub about 1 m high, much branched; leaves 4-7.5 cm broad, paler beneath, 3-5-lobed, the lobes irregularly crenate, stalked glandular-pubescent both surfaces; petioles about as long as the blades, broad at the base, glandular-pubescent; racemes mostly longer than the leaves; bracts as long as the pedicels; calyx-tube as long as the spreading lobes, pink-tinged, very little glandular; petals and stamens short; ovary mostly glabrous; berry black, glabrous, glaucous, occasionally with a few stalked-glands.

Occasional in woods east of divide. C and AT. Pole Bridge; McKenzie Pass area; Sparks L.

33. ROSACEAE   Rose Family

Herbs, shrubs, or trees; leaves alternate, simple or compound, often with stipules; calyx 5-lobed; petals 5, rarely none; stamens 10-many, usually indefinite, inserted on the calyx-tube; carpels 1-many, simple, distinct and free from the calyx, superior; or united into a 2-5-celled ovary, inferior or nearly so; fruit a follicle (pod), achene, drupe, cluster of drupelets or pome.

KEY TO THE GENERA OF ROSACEAE

Fruit of follicles, achenes or partly joined drupelets
  Fruit of 5 dehiscent follicles (those of *Holodiscus* imperfectly dehiscent)
    Leaves entire or toothed; stamens distinct; shrubs
      Follicles several-seeded; stamens well exserted ....*Spiraea*

      Follicles (or achenes) 1-seeded; stamens little exserted ....*Holodiscus*

    Leaves 2-3 times ternately-cleft; stamens united below; herbs ....*Luetkea*

  Fruit of indehiscent achenes or drupelets
    Fruit fleshy, of partly joined drupelets ....*Rubus*

    Fruit of dry achenes
      Achenes several, not enclosed in a fleshy hypanthium
        Stamens numerous
          Receptacle dry when mature, usually little enlarged in fruit (enlarged in *Comarum*), leaves not trifoliate
          Mature achenes long-beaked ....*Geum*

          Mature achenes not long-beaked

Petals red, receptacle enlarged and
  spongy in fruit..*Comarum*

Petals yellow to white, receptacle not enlarged
  and spongy in fruit..*Potentilla*

Receptacle succulent when mature, enlarged, fleshy,
  red; leaves trifoliate..*Fragaria*

Stamens 5, leaves trifoliate..*Sibbaldia*

Achenes 1; or many and enclosed in a fleshy hypanthium
  Hypanthium narrowly funnelform; fruit a solitary achene;
  leaves simple, cleft..*Purshia*

Hypanthium globose or urn-shaped, fleshy, colored, enclosing
  the many achenes, leaves pinnately compound........................*Rosa*

Fruit a drupe or pome; shrubs or trees
  Fruit a drupe, ovary superior..*Prunus*

Fruit a small berry-like pome, ovary inferior
  Leaves simple, fruit bluish-black...*Amelanchier*

Leaves pinnately compound, fruit orange or red......................*Sorbus*

AMELANCHIER Medic. Serviceberry

Shrubs or small trees; leaves simple, serrate; sepals 5; petals 5, white; stamens numerous; styles 2-5; fruit a berry-like pome.

Amelanchier florida Lindl. Bot. Reg. 19: pl. 1589. 1833. WESTERN SERVICEBERRY. Large shrub; leaves simple, oval, pubescent, serrate above the middle, 2-4 cm long; flowers in racemes, the branches and pedicels pubescent; petals white, oblanceolate, 1-1.5 cm long; fruit about 1 cm in diameter, globose, glaucous.

Frequent. H. to HT. Lake Valley; Windy Point; Obsidian Cliffs 1890 m (6200 ft); Sparks L. area.

COMARUM L.

Comarum palustre L. Sp. Pl. 502. 1753. MARSH CINQUEFOIL. Perennial herb; stems stout; rootstocks long creeping; leaves 5-7-foliate, the leaflets 2-5 cm long, oblong or oval, serrate, pale beneath and somewhat pubescent; stipules membranaceous; flowers in open cymes; calyx 5-lobed with slender shorter bractlets alternating, reddish-purple, the sepals ovate, acuminate; petals small, half as long as the sepals, narrow, acute, dark-reddish-purple; stamens numerous, reddish-purple; carpels numerous, the styles reddish-purple; receptacle enlarged, spongy, bearing the numerous achenes.

Rare in the area. Marshy places. H to T. Marshy shore of Devlis L. 1660 m (5445 ft).

FRAGARIA L.

Perennial acaulescent, stoloniferous herbs; short thick rhizomes; leaves trifoliate; sepals 5; petals 5, white, orbicular; stamens about 20; carpels numerous borne on the fleshy receptacle, in fruit becoming bright red, juicy.

Fragaria platypetala Rydb. Mem. Dept. Bot. Columbia Univ. 2:117. 1898. BROAD-PETALED STRAWBERRY. Rootstock woody; leaves glabrous above, villous and paler beneath; petioles long, villous; leaflets obovate, dentate above the middle, petioluluate; peduncles shorter than the leaves; flowers several on long pedicels; petals orbicular, white, about 6 mm long, twice as long as the sepals; fruit globose, about 13 mm in diameter, the achenes in shallow pits.

Frequent in open woods. Lower H to T. Pole Bridge; Trout Cr.

GEUM L.

Perennial herbs; stout rootstocks; leaves pinnately divided, mostly basal; sepals 5 with alternating bractlets; petals 5; stamens numerous; pistils numerous; achenes small with hooked beak.

Geum macrophyllum Willd, Enum. Hort. Ber. 557. 1809. LARGE-LEAVED AVENS. Stems 15-30 cm high, hairy; basal leaves petioled, lyrate-pinnate, the terminal leaflet round in outline, crenulate-dentate, lobed, much larger than the other leaflets which vary greatly in size and number; stem leaves small, sessile, deeply lobed, often doubly serrate; inflorescence open, few-flowered; calyx-lobes acute, reflexed; petals about 6.5 mm long, orbicular, yellow; achenes with long hooked beak.

Rare, moist grassy border of Craig L.

HOLODISCUS Maxim.

Shrubs with simple alternate leaves, lobed or serrate; sepals 5; petals 5, white, orbicular; stamens about 20 borne on a ring-like disc; carpels 5, distinct, pubescent; fruit 1-seeded (achenes).

Holodiscus glabrescens (Greenm.) Hel. Muhlenbergia 1:40. 1904. DWARF OCEAN-SPRAY. Shrub 60-150 cm high, much branched; leaves 1.3-2.5 cm long, obovate, cuneate base, toothed, sessile-glandular and somewhat villous on both surfaces; petioles winged; flowers numerous, paniculate; sepals glandular, little shorter than the petals; petals cream-white, about 2 mm long; carpels villous.

Occasional in open woods. H, C and AT. McKenzie Pass; Lake Valley; Tenas Lakes; Broken Top, above 2400 m (8000 ft); Ball Butte 2470 m (8100 ft).

LUETKEA Bong.

Luetkea pectinata (Pursh) Kuntze, Rev. Gen. Pl. 217. 1891. LUETKEA. Perennials, cespitose, decumbent; stoloniferous branches; flowering stems sparsely pubescent, 5-10 cm high; sterile shoots much lower, bearing crowded, ternately-dissected, glabrous leaves; racemes narrow, and close-flowered above; flowers several, small; petals broad-ovate, white, about 3 mm long; follicles small.

Common on higher rocky slopes and wooded areas, often forming extensive mats. A and H. Black Crater; Scott Mt.; Middle Sister; Green Lakes.

POTENTILLA L.

Mostly perennial herbs; leaves compound; flowers usually yellow, cymose; calyx 5-lobed; petals 5; stamens many; pistils several to many; fruit, achenes forming a head.

KEY TO THE SPECIES OF POTENTILLA

Basal leaves digitate
  Leaves 3-foliate..*P. flabellifolia*

  Leaves with 5 or more leaflets.................................*P. gracilis*

Basal leaves pinnate
  Style terminal
    Leaves densely-villous both sides....................*P. breweri*

    Leaves not densely-villous both sides.............*P. drummondii*

  Style basal..*P. glandulosa*

Potentilla breweri Wats. Proc. Amer. Acad. 8:555. 1873. BREWER'S CINQUEFOIL. Perennial with several stems from stout branching caudex, ascending, 15-35 cm high, wooly; basal leaves tomentose, 5-10 cm long with petioles often as long; 7-13 leaflets about 20 mm long, deeply cleft into narrow segments; cauline leaves much reduced; inflorescence several-flowered, long-pediceled, open, leafy-bracted; sepals 5, alternating with as many bracts, villous; petals 5, yellow, obcordate, about 7 mm long, longer than the sepals.

Occasional in meadows and open woods. Lower H and C. West Lava Camp; Lake Valley; Frog Camp; Sparks L.

Potentilla drummondii Lehm. Stirp. Pug. 2:9. 1830. DRUMMOND'S CINQUEFOIL. Several stems from stout branching caudex, decumbent, 25-50 cm high, thinly pubescent; leaflets 5-9, about 2.5 cm long, deeply and narrowly lobed, glabrate above, the veins beneath villous, petioles often exceeding the blades; inflorescence open, flowers on long pedicels; sepals villous, bractlets smaller, narrower; petals 5, yellow,

obcordate, 6 mm long or more; stamens about 20; pistils many, styles filiform.

Frequent in open woods and meadows. Lower H. Lake Valley; Sand Hills.

Potentilla flabellifolia Hook. ex Torr. & Gray, Fl. N. Amer. 1:442. 1840. FRINGE-LEAF CINQUEFOIL. Perennial; stems from much branched scaly rhizome, 10-25 cm high; basal leaves on long slender petioles, leaflets 3, slightly pubescent, cuneate base, deeply serrate, the blades about 2 cm long; cauline leaves 1 or 2, much reduced; cymes few-flowered; sepals 5, slightly villous, about 5 mm long, alternating with 5 bractlets about as long but more obtuse; petals yellow, obcordate, about 8 mm long; styles filiform.

Frequent in meadows and open woods. H. McKenzie Pass; Lake Valley; Camp Agoseris 1890 m (6200 ft); Spring L.

Potentilla glandulosa Lindy. Bot. Reg. 19:pl. 1583. 1838. STICKY CINQUEFOIL. Perennial with branching rhizome; stems 25-50 cm high, glandular-villous; basal pinnate leaves long-petioled with 7-9 leaflets, obovate, sparsely glandular-pubescent, serrate sometimes doubly; cauline leaves shorter petioled; inflorescence a leafy-bracted cyme; sepals glandular-pubescent, about 6 mm long, the alternating bractlets a little shorter; petals yellow, obovate, as long as the sepals.

Infrequent in open woods and meadows. H to T. Pole Bridge; Three Cr.; Green Lakes; Broken Top above 2440 m (8000 ft).

Potentilla gracilis Dougl. ex Hook. Bot. Mag. pl. 2984. 1830. SLENDER CINQUEFOIL. Stems 30-60 cm high, slender, erect, silky-villous; basal leaves with long hairy petioles, stipulate, digitate, the 5-7 leaflets 2.5-7.5 cm long, oblanceolate, pubescent above, white-tomentose beneath, deeply cut into long slender teeth; cyme many-flowered; calyx silky-villous, 5 lobed with 5 shorter more slender bractlets; petals yellow, obcordate, 0.5-1 cm long; stamens about 20; achenes numerous, smooth.

Rare in area. Lower H to T. Observed only on grassy margin of Craig L.

PRUNUS L.

Trees or shrubs; leaves simple, serrate; petals 5, white or pink, spreading; stamens about 20; pistil 1, 1-celled with 2 ovules; fruit a fleshy drupe with stony endocarp enclosing the seed.

Prunus emarginata (Dougl.) Walp. Rep. Bot. 2:9. 1843. BITTER CHERRY. A slender branched shrub, 1-4 m high; bark smooth; leaves oblong-ovate, 2-3.8 cm long, glandular-serrate, glabrous above and so beneath at maturity; flowers in small clusters; petals 5, white, obovate, about 4.5 mm long, twice as long as the calyx-lobes; drupes about 10 mm long, bright red, bitter and astringent; stone slightly pointed at each end.

Enters area from both sides of the divide, sparingly. Open woods. C to AT. Trout Cr. Butte; Windy Point.

PURSHIA DC.

Much branched shrubs with small leaves, 3-cleft at apex; flowers solitary, terminating short branches;

hypanthium turbinate; calyx 5-lobed; petals 5, yellow; stamens 15-20; pistil 1; achenes beaked.

Purshia tridentata (Pursh) DC. Trans. Linn. Soc. 12:158. 1817. BITTER OR ANTELOPE BRUSH. Shrub 60-150 cm high, or more; bark rough, gray to brown; leaves cuneate, 10-25 mm long, 3-lobed at apex, white-tomentose beneath, thinly pubescent above; flowers nearly sessile; calyx-tube funnelform, glandular; calyx-lobes rounded, reflexed; petals about 8 mm long, spatulate; achenes densely short-hairy; seeds solitary, dull black.

In dry *Pinus ponderosa* woods, often with *Artemisia*. AT. Trout Cr. Swamp; 5-6 miles north of Three Creek L. 1665 m (5460 ft).

ROSA L.

Shrubs prickly; leaves odd-pinnate with stipules adnate to the petioles; flowers large, solitary or corymbose; sepals 5; petals 5; stamens many; pistils many, enclosed in the hypanthium but distinct; ovaries hairy, becoming bony achenes.

Rosa gymnocarpa Nutt. Torr. & Gray, Fl. N. Amer. 1:461. 1840. WOOD ROSE. Shrub 60-120 cm high; stems slender with many straight, slender prickles; leaflets 5-7, elliptic, 12-20 mm long, glabrous, pale and reticulate beneath, doubly-serrate, the teeth gland-tipped; stipules narrow, glandular-ciliate, rachis prickly and glandular; flowers solitary; sepals ovate, deciduous in fruit; petals pink, about 1 cm long, rounded, spreading; hip (hypanthium) red, berry-like, about 6 mm long.

Occasional in wooded areas. Lower H to HT. West Lava Camp; Lava Camp L.; Lake Valley.

RUBUS L.

Shrubs or herbs usually with prickly stems; leaves alternate, simple or compound; flowers white or pink; sepals 5; petals 5; stamens many; pistils many on an elongated receptacle, in fruit the pulpy drupelets forming an aggregate fruit.

KEY TO THE SPECIES OF RUBUS

Stems not prickly, leaves simple
   Stems erect, flowers paniculate..*R. parviflorus*
   Stems creeping, herbaceous..*R. lasiococcus*
Stems prickly, leaves compound..*R. vitifolius*

Rubus lasiococcus Gray, Proc. Amer. Acad. 17:201. 1882. DWARF BRAMBLE. Perennial herb; stems slender, creeping, rooting at nodes, with short, erect flowering branches; leaves 3-5-lobed or divided, serrate, glabrous or with few hairs above and on veins beneath, about 4 cm broad; stipules large; flowers 1-2 on slender pedicels at the nodes; sepals acuminate; petals white, about 1 cm long, obovate; fruit pubescent, reddish, about 1 cm broad.

Frequent in woods. H and C. Scott Mt.; Frog Camp; Sims Butte; Soda Spring.

Rubus parviflorus Nutt. Gen. 1:308. 1818. THIMBLE BERRY. Shrub 0.6-1.5 m high, without prickles; bark smooth, brown, becoming shreddy; leaves 10-15 cm or more broad, palmately 5-lobed, serrate, sparsely pubescent, petioles hispid-glandular; flowers about 5, corymbose; sepals long-caudate, glandular-pubescent; petals white, about 1.5 cm long; fruit separating from the receptacle, hemispheric, red, juicy. Edible.

Frequent in woods at lower elevations. Lower H to C. Pine Butte; Lake Valley; Benson-Tenas Lakes.

Rubus vitifolius C. & S. Linnaea 2:10. 1827. WILD BLACKBERRY. Stems slender, trailing, somewhat glaucous, with slender, straight or curved prickles; leaves mostly pinnately 3-foliate, dentate, the terminal leaflet often 3-lobed, sparsely pubescent both sides; flowers dioecious, the staminate larger with elongated petals, the pistillate smaller with broad petals; fruit oblong, black, juicy, sweet. Edible.

Not common. To the west at lower altitudes abundant in old burns and logged-off areas. Mainly HT. Melakwa L.; Sims Butte.

SIBBALDIA L.

Perenial herbs, low tufted; leaves trifoliate; sepals 5 with 5 bractlets alternating; petals 5, yellow; stamens 5; pistils few with lateral styles; fruit, achenes.

Sibbaldia procumbens L. Sp. Pl. 284. 1753. SIBBALDIA. Plant low, with short branched woody base; leaves with slender petioles; leaflets appressed-villous, about 1 cm long, obovate, 3-toothed at apex, cuneate at base; stipules large, scarious; peduncles axillary, few-flowered; sepals about 3 mm long, longer than the narrow bractlets or the yellow petals.

Frequent above and below timberline. A and H. Middle Sister at 2290 m (7500 ft); South Sister at 2590 m (8500 ft); Devils L.; Matthieu Lakes 1785 m (5850 ft).

SORBUS L.

Shrubs or small trees; leaves alternate, pinnate, serrate, deciduous; flowers small in terminal compound cymes; hypanthium urn-shaped; sepals 5; petals 5, white; stamens numerous; ovary inferior, 3-celled; styles 3, distinct; ovules 2 in each cell; fruit a berry-like pome.

KEY TO THE SPECIES OF SORBUS

Leaflets serrate only near the apex, dull green, fruit glaucous.....................S. occidentalis

Leaflets serrate to near the base, bright green; fruit not glaucous................S. sitchensis

Sorbus occidentalis (Wats.) Greene, Fl. Fran. 54. 1891. DWARF MOUNTAIN ASH. Shrub 75-100 cm high; leaflets 7-9, 2.5 cm or more long, serrate at apex only or entire, oblong, dull above, the rechis and petiole sparsely pubescent; corymbs broad; flowers about 6 mm broad; fruit 6-10 mm long, nearly globose, light red or slightly purplish, glaucescent.

Occasional throughout H zone in lava beds and rocky slopes. McKenzie Pass; Lake Valley; Black Crater; Little Brother; Green Lakes.

Sorbus sitchensis Roem. Fam. Syn. Monogr. 3:139. 1847. WESTERN MOUNTAIN ASH. A large shrub, 2-4 m high; leaves 10-15 cm long, rachis and petioles pubescent; leaflets 9-13, narrow, elliptic, acute, serrate to near the base, nearly glabrous, bright green above; inflorescence a large compound cyme, pubescent; petals broad; fruit 6-10 mm long, globose, coral to red-orange.

Occasional in open woods. Lower H, C and T. Trout Cr. Swamp; Black Crater at 1585 m (5200 ft); Matthieu Lakes; Lake Valley; Soda Springs.

SPIRAEA L.

Shrubs with simple serrate leaves; flowers small in dense corymbs, racemes or panicles; sepals 5, persistent; petals 5, white or rose; stamens numerous on long filaments; pistils usually 5, distinct, forming follicles dehiscing along the ventral side; seeds few, tapering at both ends.

A *Rubus lasiococcus*; **B** *Spiraea densiflora*; **C** *Sibbaldia procumbens*;
D *Sorbus occidentalis*

KEY TO THE SPECIES OF SPIRAEA

Inflorescence round-topped, sepals not reflexed..*S. densiflora*

Inflorescence elongated, sepals reflexed
　Leaves white-tomentose beneath..*S. douglasii*

　Leaves glabrous or puberulent beneath..*S. douglasii* var. *menziesii*

Spiraea densiflora Nutt. T. & G. Fl. N. Amer. 1:414. 1840. MOUNTAIN SPIRAEA. Low shrub, much branched, about 60 cm high, glabrous; bark shining brown, peeling in thin layers; leaves elliptic, ends rounded, 2.5-4.5 cm long, serrate above the middle, short-petioled; inflorescence rounded, dense; petals 1.5 mm long, rose-colored; stamens 20 or more; follicles 5, shiny brown.

Frequent in damp meadows and near lakes and streams. H. Lava Camp L.; Lake Valley; Linton Cr. at source 1860 m (6100 ft) ; Green Lakes.

Spiraea douglassii Hook. Fl. Bor. Amer. 1:172. 1838. WESTERN SPIRAEA. Shrub 75-150 cm high; leaves elliptic, obtuse, 4.5-7.5 cm long, serrate above the middle, glabrous and green above, white tomentose beneath, short-petioled; inflorescence elongated, narrow, congested; sepals reflexed; petals rose-colored, 1.5 mm long; stamens about 20, long-exserted; follicles 5, shiny.

Occasional along streams and in meadows west of the divide. Lower H. Common in HT. Scott L. 1465 m (4800 ft).

Spiraea douglasii Hook var. **menziesii** Presl. Epim. Bot. 195. 1852. MENZIES' SPIRAEA. Leaves glabrous beneath or nearly so. Otherwise very much like the species.

Occasional in moist places. Lower H to C and T. Pole Bridge; Trout Cr. Swamp; Soda Cr. at Sparks L.

34. LEGUMINOSAE　　Pea Family

Herbs; leaves alternate, compound, stipulate; flowers irregular, papilionaceous; calyx of 5 sepals variously united; petals 5, inserted on the receptacle, the upper one (standard or banner) largest and folded over the two lateral ones (wings) in the bud, and these enclosing the two lower ones which are usually united at the apex forming the keel; stamens usually 10; pistil 1, simple; fruit a legume (pod).

KEY TO THE GENERA OF LEGUMINOSAE

Leaves even-pinnately compound ....*Lathyrus*

Leaves palmately compound
　Filaments all united, leaflets 5-12 or more ....*Lupinus*

　Filaments all but one united, leaves trifoliate ....*Trifolium*

LATHYRUS L.

Lathyrus lanszwertii Kell. var. **aridus** (Piper) Jeps. Fl. Calif. 2:389. 1936. THICK-LEAVED PEA. Perennial herb, sparingly pubescent; stems firm, erect, 15-30 cm high; leaves pinnate with 6-8 narrow linear-lanceolate leaflets, 2.5-5 cm long, puberulent both surfaces, terminating with a simple or branched tendril; racemes few-flowered; calyx-teeth unequal; corolla irregular, purple, about 10 mm long; pods glabrous, about 2.5 cm long.

Occasional in open woods east of divide. AT. Trout Cr. Swamp.

LUPINUS L.

Annual or perennial herbs; leaves alternate, palmately compound; flowers in terminal racemes; calyx bilabiate; corolla blue, purple, white or yellow; stamens 10, the filaments united, anthers of two kinds, long and short; pod flattened; seeds 2 to several.

KEY TO THE SPECIES OF LUPINUS

Low alpine perennials, spike-like racemes, pedicels under 3 mm long ......*L. lepidus lyalli*

Taller perennials, pedicels mostly over 3 mm long
　Calyx saccate or short-spurred ....*L. laxiflorus*

　Calyx not definitely saccate or spurred
　　Leaflets pubescent on both surfaces
　　　Upper margin of keel ciliate ....*L. alpicola*

　　　Keel not ciliate ....*L. andersonii*

　　Leaflets glabrous above ....*L. latifolius*

Lupinus alpicola Henderson ex Piper, Contr. U. S. Herb. 11:355. 1906. ALPINE LUPINE. Stems erect, mostly simple, appressed-pubescent; leaflets 7-9, about 5 cm long, narrowly lanceolate, acute, appressed-pubescent both sides; lower leaves long-petioled; racems up to 15 cm long, the flowers scattered, pedicels about 5 mm long; corolla light purple-blue, about 1 cm long, the keel ciliate on upper margins; pods silky-pubescent.

Rare in dry sandy soil, open woods. H .Park Meadow, west of Three Creek L 1900 m (6250 ft).

Lupinus andersonii S. Wats. Bot. King Expl. 58. 1871. ANDERSON'S LUPINE. Stems several, 30-45 cm high, rather slender, branched above, short appressed hairs; leaves all cauline; leaflets 12-50 mm long, unequal in length, oblanceolate, minute appressed hairs both surfaces; petioles short; racemes lax; pedicels 3-4.5 mm long, the bracts a little longer; flowers 10-12 mm long; corolla purplish, keel without cilia; pods appressed-hairy, 3.8 cm long.

Occasional in dry sandy soil. H to AT. Black Crater; Mathieu Lakes; Lake Valley; Green Lakes.

Lupinus latifolius Piper & Robinson var. **subalpinus** C. P. Smith, Bull. Torrey Club 51:308. 1924. SUBALPINE BROADLEAVED LUPINE. Stems several from a woody base, 25-45 cm high, simple, thinly appressed-pubescent; leaflets 6-9, 2-6.5 cm long, oblanceolate, glabrous or minutely pubescent beneath; racemes 7.5-15 cm long, loosely flowered; pedicels 4-8 mm long, silky-pubescent; corolla about 12.5 mm long, blue or purple and white, the wings broad and covering the keel, little if at all ciliate; pods about 3 cm long, densely silky-pubescent.

Frequent in open woods. H. White Branch Cr. at 1800 m (5900 ft); Sunshine Shelter; South Sister; Green Lakes.

Lupinus laxiflorus Dougl. ex Lindl. Bot. Reg. 14:pl.1140. 1826. DOUGLAS' SPURRED LUPINE. Stems several from woody base, 30-60 cm high, thinly appressed-pubescent; leaflets 7-9, 3.8-5 cm long, appressed-pubescent both surfaces, narrowly oblanceolate; racems about 15 cm long, loosely flowered; pedicels 3-5 mm long; calyx with well developed spur above, densely appressed-pubescent; corolla about 1 cm long, blue to purple, the wings glabrous, the keel ciliate on the upper edges; pods about 2.5 cm long, silky-pubescent.

Barely enters area on the east side. AT. Trout Cr. road; Sisters-Sparks L. road at 1585 m (5200 ft).

Lupinus lepidus Dougl. ssp. **lyallii** (Gray) Detl. Amer. Mid. Nat. 45:490. 1951. LYALL'S LUPINE. Cespitose plants with short, prostrate, woody branches; leaflets 5 or 6, 8-14 mm long, appressed silkly-pubescent both surfaces, on long petioles; racemes above the leaves, 2-3.8 cm. long; flower purple-blue, 8-12 mm long, the standard white, the keel ciliate on upper margin; pods silky-pubescent.

Common in dry open woods in sa ndy soil. H. Lake Valley; Park Meadow; Green Lakes; Wickiup Plain 1922 m (6300 ft.)

TRIFOLIUM L.

Annual or perennial herbs; leaves palmately trifoliate; flowers purple, white or yellow, in heads; calyx 5-toothed; stamens in two groups; pods mostly enclosed by the calyx.

Trifolium longipes Nutt. in Torr. & Gray, Fl. N. Amer. 1:314. 1838. LONG-STALKED CLOVER. Perennial; stems erect, slender, simple, 10-30 cm high; leaflets oblong to linear-lanceolate, 1.2-3.2 cm long, entire or minutely spinulose, glabrous above, thinly pubescent beneath; petioles long on the lowest leaves, shorter on the upper; stipules long, foliaceous; heads on long peduncles; calyx villous, the teeth much longer than the tube; corolla white or light yellowish, 1-1.5 cm long.

Frequent in meadows. H to T. Lake Valley; Three Creek L; Sparks L.

35. CELASTRACEAE   Staff-Tree Family

PACHYSTIMA Raf.

Low evergreen shrub; twigs 4-angled; leaves opposite, coriaceous, serrulate; ffowers small, 4-merous, clustered in the leaf axils.

Pachystima myrsinites (Pursh) Raf. Fl. Tellur. 42. 1838. OREGON BOXWOOD. Low much branched shrub, glabrous, 60-90 cm high, very leafy; leaves narrowly elliptic to obovate, serrulate, 1.3-2.5 cm long, short-petioled; flowers minute; calyx-lobes rounded; petals dark brownish-red; stamens 4; capsule 2-celled; seeds 2, black with a much-lobed aril at base.

Frequent in woods. Lower H and C. Pine Butte; Frog Camp; Windy Point; Little Brother; Sparks L.

36. ACERACEAE   Maple Family

ACER L.

Trees or shrubs; le aves opposite, petioled, deciduous; ca lyx usually 5-lobed; petals same number as calyx-lobes or none; disk lobed, thick, flat; stamens usually 7-10 or fewer; pistil 1, ovary superior, 2-celled, each with 2 ovules; styles 2 spreading and distinct or joined at base, each with terminal stigma; fruit of 2 long-winged samaras joined at base, separating at maturity.

KEY TO THE SPECIES OF ACER

Leaves 7-9 lobed; samaras widely spreading
about 180 degrees; sepals dark red...*A. circinatum*

Leaves 3-5 lobed; samaras spreading less than
90 degrees; sepals yellowish-green.............................*A. glabrum subsp. douglasii*

Acer circinatum Pursh. Fl. Amer. Sept. 1:267. 1814. VINE MAPLE. A large shrub, often vine-like; bark smooth; leaves round or cordate in outline, 6-8 cm broad, 7-9 palmately-lobed, the lobes serrate, glabrous at maturity; corymbs 8-20 flowered, terminal on slender branchlets; sepals sparsely villous; petals whitish, shorter than the sepals; stamens 8, long-exserted; fruit glabrous, wings about 2.5 cm long, spreading 180 degrees.

Observed only at Melakwa L. Common along wooded streams in HT.

Acer glabrum Torr. subsp. **douglasii** (Hook.) Wesml. Bull. Bot. Soc. Belg. 29:46. 1890. DOUGLAS MAPLE. Shrubby tree, usually growing to a height not exceeding 6 m (20 ft); bark gray, smooth; leaves 5-10 cm long and as wide, glabrous, paler beneath, variable but usually 3- or 5-lobed, the lobes irregularly serrate or sometimes dentate; petioles slender, longer than the blades; corymbs 5-10-flowered; sepals and petals similar, about 3 mm long, light greenish; filaments shorter than the petals; samars glabrous, about 2.5 cm long, the wings spreading 90 degrees or less.

Rare in area. Lower H to C. Windy Point 1495 m (4900 ft) and lower.

37. RHAMNACEAE   Buckthorn Family

Shrubs or small trees; leaves alternate, simple, deciduous or evergreen.

KEY TO THE GENERA OF RHAMNACEAE

Fruit a capsule; petals distinctly clawed..*Ceanothus*

Fruit a berry-like drupe; petals without claws..*Rhamnus*

CEANOTHUS L.

Shrubs with usually 3-nerved, coriaceous leaves; flowers small in clusters, white or blue.

Ceanothus velutinus Dougl. Hook. Fl. Bor. Amer. 1:125. 1830. BUCK BRUSH or SNOW BRUSH. Shrub 1-2.5 m. high, much branched, widely spreading; leaves evergreen, 5-7.5 cm long, oval, obtuse, dark green and sticky-varnished above with strong aromatic odor, lighter and velvety beneath, the 3 prominent veins pubescent, the margin glandular-denticulate, petioles short; flowers white in panicles, branches puberulent; capsules 3-lobed above, nearly smooth.

Occasional, especially in *Pinus ponderosa* woods. Lower H to T. Pine Butte; south of Black Pine Spring.

RHAMNUS L.

Shrubs or small trees; leaves alternate, pinnately-veined; flowers small, in axillary clusters; calyx 4-5-lobed; petals 4-5; stamens 4-5; fruit a berry-like drupe with 2-4 one-seeded nutlets.

Rhamnus purshiana DC. Prodr. 2:25. 1825. CASCARA. Usually a small tree not over 7.5 m (25 ft) high; bark smooth, gray; leaves deciduous, oblong-ovate, 5-10 cm long, denticulate, glabrous above, pubescent beneath, petioles rather short; flowers 5-merous, about 3 mm wide, greenish; petals short-clawed, truncate; fruit black, of 3 nutlets.

Infrequent on lower slopes. Lower H to T. Benson L. 1615 m (5300 ft); Four Mile Spring road area.

38. HYPERICACEAE   St. John's-wort Family

HYPERICUM L.

Herbs or shrubs; leaves sessile, opposite, glandular-dotted; sepals 5; petals 5; stamens numerous, distinct or united in clusters; ovary 1-celled; capsule dehiscent; seeds numerous.

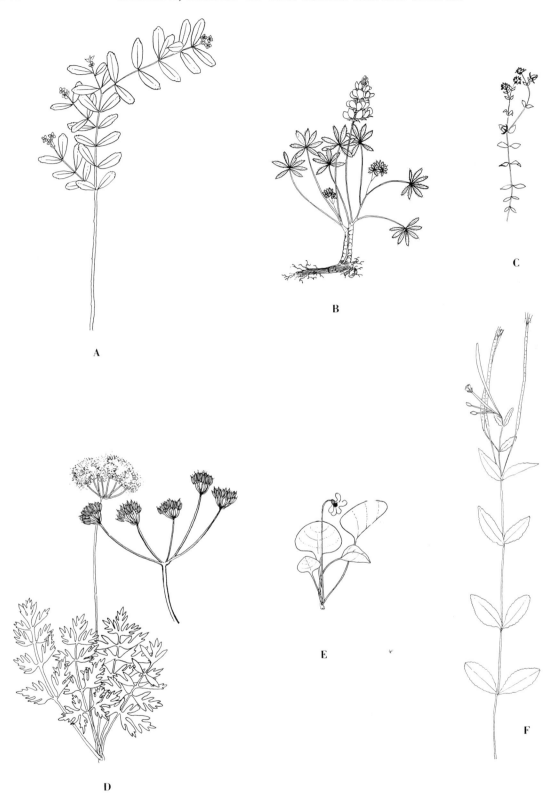

A *Pachystima myrsinites;* **B** *Lupinus lepidus lyallii;* **C** *Hypericum anagalliodes;*
D *Ligusticum grayi;* **E** *Viola macloskeyi;* **F** *Epilobium hornmannii*

KEY TO THE SPECIES OF HYPERICUM

Stems weak; petals orange-yellow, not black-dotted on
  the margin, not longer than the sepals...*H. anagalloides*

Stems rigid, erect; petals yellow, black-dotted on
  the margin, much longer than the sepals...*H. scouleri*

Hypericum anagalloides C & S. Linnaea 3:127. 1828. BOG ST. JOHN'S-WORT. Low perennial forming mats; stems slender, weak, simple or branched; leaves opposite, sessile, ovate, obtuse, 3-8 mm long; flowers solitary or in few-flowered cymes; sepals shorter or equaling the small oval petals; stamens about 15; capsure about 3 mm long, 1-celled.

Frequent in moist meadows. Lower H to HT. Lake Valley; Frog Camp; Sparks L.

Hypericum scouleri Hook. Fl. Bor. Am. 1:111. 1830. WESTERN ST. JOHN'S-WORT. Perennial herb, erect, 20-60 cm high; leaves ovate to lanceolate, obtuse, 1.5-2.5 cm long, entire, sessile, somewhat clasping; flowers in cymes at the end of branches; sepals about 3 mm long; petals about 8 mm long; stamens many, anthers black-dotted; capsule 6 mm long, 3-celled, 3-lobed.

Frequent in wet ground. Lower H to T. Craig L. 1550 m (5100 ft); Fall Cr.; Soda Spring.

39. VIOLACEAE   Violet Family

VIOLA L.

Low herbs; leaves alternate or basal, simple, stipulate; flowers solitary or clustered, perfect, irregular; petals 5, the lower spurred; stamens 5, the two lower with appendages extending into the spur of the petal, hypogynous; filaments short or none; anthers erect, connivent; ovary solitary, 1-celled; capsule 3-sided, many-seeded.

KEY TO THE SPECIES OF VIOLA

Flowers blue or white
  Acaulescent, leaves orbicular or reniform
    very small plants, petals white, leaves mostly entire ....*V. macloskeyi*

    Larger plants, petals light purple to white
      leaves crenate...*V. palustris*

    Caulescent, leaves ovate, flowers blue...*V. adunca*

Flowers yellow at least on inner surface
  Stems erect, flowers crowded near apex.......................................*V. glabella*

  Stems prostrate or erect, flowers and leaves
      not crowded at apex
    Leaves distinctly cordate at base;
      reniform or orbicular...*V. orbiculata*

  Leaves not distinctly cordate at base; longer than broad
    Petals yellow, tinged red or purple without, or purple-
      veined, leaves usually coarsely dentate ....*V. purpurea*

    Petals bright-yellow, purple-veined, leaves entire or remotely
      crenate-dentate...*V. praemorsa*

Viola adunca Smith in Rees, Cycl. 37:no. 63. 1817. WESTERN BLUE VIOLET. Rootstock branching; stems ascending, very short or to 10 cm long; plant glabrous or puberulent; leaves ovate with truncate or cordate base, crenate, 1-3.8 cm long on long petioles, stipules lacerate; flowers violet-blue, the spur about half as long as the blades.

Common in meadows and woods. H to T. Lake Valley; Skyline Trail south of Sunshine Shelter at 1986 m (6500 ft); Sparks L.

Viola glabella Nutt. Torr. & Gray. Fl. 1:142. 1838. SMOOTH WOOD VIOLET. Rootstocks horizontal; stems mostly glabrous, rarely longer than 12 cm; stem leaves 2 or more, reniform-cordate, crenate-serrate, 2.5-4.5 cm broad on petioles about as long, glabrous; basal leaves similar, on long petioles; petals yellow, the lower purple-veined, about 1 cm. long, spur short, saccate. Much larger plants are found at lower elevations.

Occasional in woods and meadows. H to HT. Huckleberry L.; Frog Camp; Obsidian Cliffs 1890 m (6200 ft).

Viola macloskeyi Lloyd, Erythea 3:74. 1895. SMALL WHITE VIOLET. Plants small, glabrous; leaves broadly ovate, slightly crenate, 2.5 cm broad or smaller; peduncles exceeding the leaves, with minute bracts below the middle; petals white, purple-veined, the lateral pair sparsely tufted at base; spur short.

Frequent in moist meadows or open woods. H and C. Lake Valley; Melakwa L.; Goose Cr. near Sparks L.

Viola orbiculata Geyer, Hook. Lond. Journ. Bot. 6:73. 1847. ROUND-LEAVED VIOLET. Rootstocks short, stout; plant glabrous; stems equaling or surpassing the leaves; leaves cordate or reniform, glabrous, 3 cm or less broad, crenate; petals yellow with purple veins, the lateral little or not bearded.

Occasional in meadows and woods. Lower H and C. Lava Camp L.; Frog Camp. Obsidian Cliffs.

Viola palustris L. Sp. Pl. 2:934. 1753 MARSH VIOLET. Plants with slender creeping rootstocks; stolons slender; leaves cordate-reniform, 5 cm broad, shallow-crenate, long-petioled; flowers pale violet; petals 1 cm long, the lateral two bearded, spur short saccate.

Rare in area. Wet Ground. C. to HT. Trout Cr. Swamp.

Viola purpurea Kell. subsp. **geophyta** Baker & Claus. Madrono 10:124.1949. PURPLE-TINTED VIOLET. Rootstocks rather stout; stems clustered, short, pubescent; leaves ovate, pubescent, strongly and irregularly toothed; flowers bright yellow, bronze or pubplish on outer surface, lateral petals tufted at base of blade; spur saccate, short.

Frequent in Trout Cr. area in *Pinus ponderosa* forest. C and AT.

Viola praemorsa Dougl. var. **linguafolia** (Nutt.) Peck, Man. Pl. Oreg. 486. 1941. UPLAND YELLOW VIOLET. Rootstock vertical, fleshy; stems short, retrorsely pubescent; leaves long-petioled, lanceolate, 5 cm long, retrorsely pubescent on veins and margin, entire or remotely toothed; petals yellow, some brownish-purple veined; capsule may be short-pubescent.

Common in dry open woods. Lower H to AT. Frog Camp; West Lava Camp; Soda Cr.; Trout Cr.

40. ONAGRACEAE Evening Primrose Family

Flowers small to rather large; stem not slender-wiry; seeds with tuft of hair (coma) at one end...........*Epilobium*

Flowers very small; stems slender-wiry; seeds without coma...........*Gayophytum*

EPILOBIUM L. Willow-herb

Perennial herbs; leaves alternate or opposite; flowers axillary or in terminal racemes or panicles; sepals 4; petals 4, white, pink, or rarely yellow; stamens 8, alternate ones with shorter filaments; stigma 4-lobed or oblong; fruit a 4-celled capsule.

KEY TO THE SPECIES OF EPILOBIUM

Flowers large; petals spreading; calyx
    cleft to the ovary...*E. angustifolium*

Flowers smaller; petals ascending; calyx-tube
    extending beyond the ovary
  Plant glaucous, glabrous or with thin-pubescent
    lines on stem: leaves pale green.................................*E. glaberrimum*

  Plant not glaucous; leaves green or canescent
   Leaves sessile, narrow, oblong, little
    spreading; stems slender...*E. oregonense*

   Leaves short-petioled and spreading
    Densely cespitose; leaves 1-2 cm long,
     ovate; capsules narrow-
     clavate; seeds papillate...*E. clavatum*

    Not densely cespitose; leaves 1.5-5 cm long
     Petals pink to purple
      Stems decumbent below; inflores-
      cence nodding..*E. alpinum*

      Stems usually not decumbent;
      inflorescence not nodding.................................*E. hornemannii*

     Petals cream-white or pale pink;
     seeds smooth...*E. lactiflorum*

Epilobium angustifolium L. Sp. Pl. 1:347. 1753. FIREWEED. Plant 45 cm or more high; short-pubescent above; leaves alternate, long, narrowly elliptic; flowers large, rose-pink or purplish in a many-flowered raceme; capsules to 9 cm long.

Occasional in dry open woods. Lower H to T. Obsidian Trail 1710 m (5600 ft); Lake Valley; Sparks L.

Epilobium glaberrimum Barbey, Bot. Calif. 1:220. 1876. SMOOTH WILLOW-HERB. Plant 15-45 cm high; glaucous and usually glabrous; leaves lanceolate; flowers few, small, pink-purple to white; seeds minutely papillose.

Infrequent in moist places. H to T. McKenzie Pass area 1615 m (5300 ft); Obsidian Cliffs; Soda Cr.

Epilobium oregonense Haussk. Monog. Epil. 276. 1884. OREGON WILLOW-HERB. 7:5-15 cm high; stems slender, simple, erect; glabrous or with lines of pubescence; flowers 1 to 3, small, pink to purplish; seeds smooth.

Infrequent in moist places. H and C. West Lava Camp; Middle Sister 2200 m (7200 ft); South Sister (W. side) 1830 m (6000 ft).

Epilobium clavatum Trel. Rep. Mo. Gard. 2:111. pl. 48. 1891. CLUB-FRUITED WILLOW-HERB. 5-10 cm high, densely matted; leaves ovate-elliptic, obtuse, subentire, glabrous; petals rose-pink; seeds papillose.

Epilobium alpinum L. Sp. Pl. 1:348. 1753. ALPINE WILLOW-HERB. E. anagallidifolium Lam. Dict. 2:376. 1786.) 7.5-15 cm high; stems numerous, bent, simple; leaves small, oblong-ovate; flowers few, small, pink, nodding; seeds smooth.

Occasional in moist places. A and H. Sunshine Shelter; upper Squaw Cr. 1830 m (6000 ft); Green Lakes; Scott L.

Epilobium hornemannii Reich. Ic. Bot. Crit. 2:73. 1824. HORNEMANN'S WILLOW-HERB. 12-30 cm high; lines of pubescence extending down from the leaf bases; leaves oblong-elliptic, glabrous; flowers few, pink-purple or white; seeds papillose.

Frequent along stream banks. H. Frog Camp; Scott Mt. 1870 m (6125 ft); Black Crater 1830 m (6000 ft); West Lava Camp; Spring L.; Three Creek L.; Green Lakes; Mesa Cr. 1770 m (5800 ft); Linton Spgs.

Epilobium lactiflorum Haussk. Oest. Bot. Zeitschr. 29;89. 1879. WHITE-FLOWERED WILLOW-HERB. 10-40 cm high, erect, slender; leaves thin, elliptic or long-ovate; denticulate to subentire; petals white or pinkish; seeds smooth.

Occasional in moist places. A to C. Scott L.; west base of Sisters 1830-2135 m (6-7000 ft); south side South Sister.

GAYOPHYTUM Juss.

Slender much-branched annuals; leaves alternate, small, narrow; flowers minute, petals usually red (or white turning red); stamens 8, the alternate one shorter; seeds many.

KEY TO THE SPECIES OF GAYOPHYTUM

Seeds strigose-pubescent..*G. lasiospermum*

Seeds glabrous..*G. nuttallii*

Gayophytum lasiospermum Greene. Pittonia 2:164. 1891. HAIRY-SEEDED GAYOPHYTUM. 15-30 cm high, petals white turning rose; capsules 6-10 mm long on sort pedicels, seeds strigose.

Infrequent in dry places. H. West Lava Camp; Soda Spg.; McKenzie Pass lava beds 1615 m (5300 ft).

Gayophytum nuttallii Torr. and Gray. Fl. N. Am. 1:514. 1840. NUTTALL'S GAYOPHYTUM. 15-30 cm high, petals pink to rose; capsules torulose, about 1 cb long on pedicsel half as long; seeds glabrous.

Infrequent in dry places. Lower H to T. McKenzie Pass; Devil's L.; Park Meadow 1875 m (6150 ft); Todd L.; West Lava Camp.

41. UMBELLIFERAE   Carrot Family

Herbs with hollow stems; leaves alternate, compound, the petioles often dilated at base; inflorescense a compound or simple umbel, usually with an involucre, the umbellets with involucels; sepals 5 or obsolete; petals 5; stamens 5; ovary inferior, 2-celled with one ovule in each cell; styles 2. Fruit of 2 dry seed-like carpels which separate when mature along the plane of their adjoining inner surfaces (the *commissure*), each carpel ribbed or winged lengthwise, usually with oil tubes between the ribs and on the side of the commissure.

KEY TO THE GENERA OF UMBELLIFERAE

Flowers in compound umbels
   Fruit 8 or more times longer than wide...*Osmorhiza*

   Fruit about 2 times longer than wide
     Fruit flattened dorsally, the lateral
      ribs broadly winged..*Lomatium*

   Fruit slightly flattened laterally
     ribs prominent...*Ligusticum*

Flowers in umbellate heads
   Umbels few-rayed, irregular, involucrate
     and with involucels, fruit
     covered with hooked bristles..*Sanicula*

   Umbels 6-12-rayed, involucre none, fruit
     more or less tomentose...*Sphenosciadium*

LIGUSTICUM L.

Ligusticum grayi C & R. Rev. N. Am. Umbell. 88. 188. GRAY'S LOVAGE. Perennial, glabrous, 25-75 cm high or more; leaves all basal except one, ternate-pinnate, the leaflets parted and cleft; rays of the umbel 10-18; fruit oval-oblong; ribs narrowly winged.

Common in meadows and open places. H and C.

Hand L.; Sunshine Shelter; Little Brother 2290 m (7500 ft); Todd L.

LOMATIUM Raf.

Perennial herbs with fleshy roots; leaves ternate or pinnate; umbels compound; involucres mostly none.

KEY TO THE SPECIES OF LOMATIUM

Plant glabrous or nearly so
   Fruit 10-12 cm long, wings about
     equaling the body...*L. martindalei*

   Fruit 8-10 cm long, wings very narrow.................................*L. angustatum*

Plant puberulent or canescent...*L. triternatum*

Lomatium angustatum (C & R) St. John, Mazama 11:83. 1929. CASCADE LOMATIUM. Plant 15-45 cm high, glabrous, with long slender tap-root; leaves ternate, then 2-3-pinnate; flowers white or yellowish; involucre and involucels wanting; fruit narrowly-oblong, 6-10 mm long.

Frequent on open rocky slopes. H. Black Crater at 2185 m (7150 ft); Frog Camp; Middle Sister at 2135 m (7000 ft); Green Lakes.

Lomatium martindalei C & R, Contr. U. S. Nat. Herb 7:225. 1900. MARTINDALE'S LOMATIUM. Plant 10-25 cm high, glabrous; fleshy tap-root; leaves bipinnate; petals yellow or white; fruit oblong, with wide wings.

Common in sandy soil. H. Black Crater; Pine Butte; Frog Camp; Fall Cr.

Lomatium triternatum (Pursh) C & R, Contr. U. S. Nat. Herb. 7:227. 1900. NARROW-LEAVED LOMATIUM. Plant 15-60 cm high, minutely puberulent; leaves triternate, leaflets linear; petals yellow; fruit glabrous, oblong, wings narrower than the body.

Occasional in Trout Cr. area. T.

OSMORHIZA Raf.

Perennial herbs; leaves ternate, the divisions serrate to lobed; flowers in few-rayed umbels, white, purplish or greenish; fruit linear-oblong.

KEY TO THE SPECIES OF OSMORHIZA

Fruit bristly, abruptly beaked, long-
   attenuate at base..*O. chilensis*

Fruit glabrous, not beaked, obtuse at base.............................*O. occidentalis*

Osmorhiza chilensis Hook. & Arn. Bot. Beechey 26. 1830. MOUNTAIN SWEET CICELY. (*Osmorhiza nuda* Torr. Pacif. R. Rep. 41:93. 1857.) Plant 15-60 cm high; leaves biternate, leaflets broad, deeply serrate or cleft; umbels 3-8-rayed; petals greenish-white.

Occasional in woods. H to T. Black Crater; Frog Camp; Trout Cr. road.

Osmorhiza occidentalis (Nutt.) Torr. Bot. Mex. Bound. 71. 1859. WESTERN SWEET CICELY. Plant 30-60 cm or more high; leaves 1-3-ternate, leaflets long-ovate, serrate, some lobed; flowers greenish; fruit 12-15 mm long.

Infrequent in woods. Lower H to T. Soda Cr. at 1740 m (5700 ft).

SANICULA L.

Perennial herbs, glabrous or pubescent; stems with few leaves, palmately or pinnately divided; umbels irregularly compound, few-rayed, with involucres and involucels; sepals foliaceous, persistent; fruit subglobose, covered with hooked bristles, not ribbed.

Sanicula bipinnatifida Dougl. ex Hook. Fl. Bor. Amer. 1:258, pl. 92. 1832. PURPLE SANICLE. Plant 15-45 cm high, glabrous; fleshy rootstocks; leaves mostly basal, pinnately divided, the divisions lobed or cleft; rachis winged, toothed; branches bearing umbels, 2-6-rayed; flowers dark purple.

Rare on open rocky slopes. H to T. Soda Cr. 1740 m (5700 ft).

SPHENOSCIADIUM Gray

Perennials, simple stout stems, glabrous to the influorescence; leaves bipinnately compound with strongly inflated patioles; flowers in dense umbellate heads without involucres, the involucels of bristle-like bracelets; sepals obsolete.

Sphenosciadium capitellatum A. Gray, Proc. Amer. Acad. 6:537. 1866. SWAMP WHITE-HEADS. Plant 30-150 cm high; inflorescence tomentose; basal leaves 15-60 cm or more long; flowers pinkish; fruit wedge-shaped, hairy, about 5 mm long.

Rare along streams east of divide. Lower H to AT. Three Creek L. area at 1970 m (6450 ft).

A *Lomatium martindalei;* **B** *Arctostaphylos nevadensis;* **C** *Osmorhiza chilensis*
D *Gaultheria humifusa;* **E** *Cassiope mertensiana*

42. CORNACEAE   Dogwood Family

CORNUS L.

Trees, shrubs, herbs; leaves opposite or whorled; cymes or heads subtended by large petaloid bracts; calyx minute, 4-lobed; petals 4; stamens 4; ovary 2-celled; fruit a 2-celled drupe with a 2-seeded stone.

KEY TO THE SPECIES OF CORNUS

Herb, inflorencence bracteate, fruit bright red..*C. canadensis*
Shrub, inflorescence not bracteate,
    fruit bluish-white...*C. stolonifera*

Cornus canadensis L. Sp. Pl. 1:118. 1753. BUNCHBERRY. Herb, 10-15 cm high; 2-3 pairs of leaves in whorl at summit of stem, one pair below; leaves elliptic or ovate, 3.5-5 cm long, acute apex and base, entire, about sessile; flowers in heads subtended by 4 white involucral bracts, broad ovate, 12-20 mm long; flowers minute, corolla purplish; fruit globose, bright red, about 5 mm in diameter.

Rare in woods. Lower H to HT. West Lava Camp 1535 m (5036 ft).

Cornus stolonifera Michx. Fl. Bor. Amer. 1:92. 1803. CREEK DOGWOOD. Shrub, 2-3 m high; branches dark red, mostly glabrous; leaves ovate-lanceolate, acute, 5-7.5 cm long, pale beneath, appressed-pubescent both surfaces; petals white; drupe globose.

Rare in the area. C and AT. Trout Cr. Swamp.

43. ERICACEAE   Heath Family

Herbs, shrubs or trees; leaves simple, alternate or opposite, evergreen or deciduous; flowers mostly regular, perfect, parts in 4's or 5's; stamens free from the corolla, as many or twice as many as the lobes; anthers opening by apical tubes or terminal pores; style simple; ovary 1-10-celled; fruit a capsule, berry or drupe.

KEY TO THE GENERA OF ERICACEAE

Ovary inferior; corolla united; fruit a berry ....*Vaccinium*
Ovary superior
  Herbs
    Without green foliage..*Hypopitys*
    Mostly with evergreen foliage
      Flowers racemose; petals more or less
        converging; filaments not dilated..*Pyrola*
      Flowers corymbose; petals spreading; filaments dilated...............*Chimaphila*
  Shrubs or trees; corolla sympetalous (petals united)
  Corolla rotate, not narrowed at the throat
    Leaves opposite...*Kalmia*
    Leaves alternate...*Rhododendron*
  Corolla urn- or bell-shaped
    Low heath-like shrubs, leaves very small
      Flowers solitary in the leaf axils;
        leaves scale-like, 4-ranked; anthers with recurved awns ....*Cassiope*
      Flowers in terminal clusters; leaves linear,
        alternate; anthers awnless ....*Phyllodoce*
    Not heath-like shrubs, leaves broad
      Calyx becoming large and fleshy,
        enclosing the berry-like many-seeded capsule ....*Gaultheria*
      Calyx small, dry; fruit a berry-
        like 5-10-seeded drupe...*Arctostaphylos*

ARCTOSTAPHYLOS Adans

Evergreen shrubs with smooth red-brown exfoliating bark; leaves alternate, coriaceous; flowers small, in terminal racemes; sepals 5, distinct; corolla urceolate, white, pink-tinged, 5-lobed; fruit a berry-like drupe.

KEY TO THE SPECIES OF ARCTOSTAPHYLOS

Shrubs depressed, often creeping; leaves oblanceolate, 0.6-1.2 cm wide, 1.5-2.4 cm long or less.................................*A. nevadensis*

Shrubs erect; leaves ovate, 2.5x3.6 cm or smaller.................................*A. patula*

Arctostaphylos nevadensis Gray, Syn. Fl. 2:27. 1878. PINE-MAT MANZANITA. Low shrub, the branches forming mats; fruit globose, red.

Frequent on rocky slopes. H and C. Windy Point; Obsidian Cliffs; Rock Mesa; Green Lakes; Black Crater; Lake Valley.

Arctostaphylos patula Greene, Pittonia 2:171. 1891. GREEN MANZANITA. Shrubs 1-1.5 m high; fruit depressed- globose, brown.

Occasional in open woods and lava beds. H to AT. McKenzie Pass 1620 m (5300 ft); Craig Monument; Lake Valley; Sparks L.; Black Pine Spg.; Black Crater.

CASSIOPE D. Don

Cassiope mertensiana (Bong.) G. Don, Gen. Syst. 3:829. 1834. WESTERN MOUNTAIN HEATHER. Low creeping shrub; leaves scale-like; corolla bell-shaped, white; fruit a capsule.

Occasional, often abundant at high altitudes. Infrequent in Lower areas. A to lower H. Middle Sister 2285 m (7500 ft); Obsidian Trail; Tenas Lakes; Green Lakes; Ball Butte.

CHIMAPHILA Pursh.

Herbaceous or slightly woody perennials with horizontal rhizomes; leaves opposite or in whorls, serrate, short-petioled; flowers in terminal racemes; sepals 5; petals 5, white or pinkish; stamens 10; ovary 5-lobed; capsule dehiscent, 5-celled; seeds minute, numerous.

KEY TO THE SPECIES OF CHIMAPHILA

Leaves variable, elliptic to ovate, 3 cm or less long; enlarged lower part of filament hairy .. ..*C. menziesii*

Leaves oblanceolate, 3-5 cm long; enlarged lower part of filaments ciliate on the margins ....*C. umbellata*

Chimaphila menziesii (R. Br.) Spreng. Syst. 2:317. 1825. LITTLE PRINCE'S PINE. PIPSISSEWA. Plant erect, 10-12 cm high; petals white or red-tinged; filaments with enlarged bases, hairy.

Rare in area in woods. C and T. Trout Cr. road; Black Pine Spg. 1475 m (4830 ft).

Chimaphila umbellata (L.) Nutt. var **occidentalis** (Rydb.) Blake, Rhodora 19:242. 1917. WESTERN PRINCE'S PINE. Plant about 15 cm high, the lower stem decumbent; petals pink or red-tinged; filaments dilated at base, the bases ciliate on the margins.

Infrequent in woods. Lower H to T. Lake Valley; Sims Butte; Matthieu L. trail; Black Pine Spg.

GAULTHERIA L.

Low evergreen shrubs, prostrate; leaves alternate, coriaceous; flowers solitary in the axils; calyx deeply 5-lobed; corolla urceolate; stamens 10; ovary 5-celled; fruit a capsule enclosed by the fleshy calyx-tube making it berry-like; seeds numerous.

KEY TO THE SPECIES OF GAULTHERIA

Calyx glabrous; leaves elliptic, oval to round oval, 9-15 mm long, obscurely denticulate or entire, apex obtuse; corolla little longer than the calyx ....*G. humifusa*

Calyx pubescent, the hairs long, sparse, spreading; leaves ovate, 18-25 mm long or more, serrate, apex acute; corolla twice as long as the calyx ....*G. ovatifolia*

Gaultheria humifusa (Graham) Rydb. Mem. N. Y. Bot. Gard. 1:300. 1900. MATTED GAULTHERIA. WINTERGREEN. Low creeping shrub, the branches rooting; flowers few; fruit bright red.

Frequent in moist ground near lakes and streams. H. Lake Valley; Spring L.; Todd L.; Matthieu L. South Sister 1860 m (6100 ft).

Gaultheria ovatifolia Gray, Proc. Amer. Acad. 19:85. 1883. OREGON SPICY WINTERGREEN. Low spreading shrub, the branches not rooting; fruit bright red.

Rare in this area in woods. Lower H (mostly C and T). Benson L.

HYPOPITYS Hill

Hypopitys fimbriata (Gray) Howell, Fl. N. W. Amer. 429. 1901. FRINGED PINESAP. Plant saprophytic, 10-20 cm high, yellowinsh, red-tinged, finely pubescent; leaves small, scale-like; flowers in a terminal raceme, usually rather crowded, on somewhat shorter pedicels, nodding, becoming erect in fruit.

Occasional in woods. H to T. Condon Butte 1800

m (5900 ft); Melakwa L.; Frog Camp; Rock Mesa; South Sister 2050 m (6700 ft); Green Lakes.

KALMIA L.

Low shrubs; leaves evergreen, coriaceous, opposite, dark green above, pale beneath, entire, revolute; flowers in terminal clusters on long slender pedicels; calyx 5-parted; corolla saucer-shaped, the lobes broad; stamens 10, included; ovary 5-celled; style slender; capsule globose.

Kalmia microphylla (Hook.) Heller, Bull. Torrey Club 25:581. 1898. KALMIA. Shrubs, much branched, 10-20 cm high; leaves about 12 mm long, glabrous, oval; corolla almost white to rose-purple, about 10 mm wide.

Frequent in swampy areas. H. Scott L.; McKenzie Pass area 1615 m (5300) ft;) Tenas Lakes; Todd L.; Three Creek L.; Sparks L.

PHYLLODOCE Salisb.

High mountain shrubs, small, clustered, evergreen; leaves needle-like.

KEY TO THE SPECIES OF PHYLLODOCE

Corolla rose-colored, bell-shaped..*P. empetriformis*

Corolla yellowish to greenish-white, urceolate...*P. glanduliflora*

Phyllodoce empetriformis (Smith) D. Don, Edinb. New Phil. Journ. 17.160. 1834. PINK MOUNTAIN HEATHER. Low branched shrub forming mats; corolla glabrous; sepals obtuse.

Frequent above and below timberline, often abundant. A and H. Tenas Lakes; Sunshine Shelter; Middle Sister 2290 m (7500 ft); near Green Lakes 2290 m (7500 ft); North Sister; West Lava Camp.

Phyllodoce glanduliflora (Hook.) Coville, Mazama 1:196. 1897. YELLOW MOUNTAIN HEATHER. Low branched matted shrub; corolla glandular-pubescent; sepals acute.

Infrequent on rocky slopes, mostly below timberline. H and A. North Sister; Black Crater; Obsidian Cliffs; Obsidian Falls; Green Lakes; Ball Butte 2470 m (8100 ft); South Sister ca 2135 m (7000 ft).

PYROLA (Tourn.) L. Wintergreen

Perennia with slender rootstocks; flowering stems simple; leaves basal, broad, evergreen; calyx 5-lobed; petals 5, concave, distinct; stamens 10, inverted, with 2 basal pores above; stigma 5-lobed; ovary 5-celled; fruit a capsule, depressed-globose.

KEY TO THE SPECIES OF PYROLA

Style bent at base, curved, with a collar
      below the stigma..*P. dentata* var

Style straight, without a collar below
      the stigma
      Style exerted, longer than 3 mm; racemes
      one-sided; petals white..*P. secunda*

Style included, not longer than 3 mm;
      racemes not secund; petals
      white or pinkish..*P. minor*

A *Hypopitys fimbriata;* **B** *Kalmia microphylla;* **C** *Phyllodoce empetriformis;*
D *Pyrola secunda;* **E** *Rhododendron albiflorum;* **F** *Vaccinium deliciosum*

Pyrola dentata Sm var. **integra** Gray, Pac. R. Rep. 12²:54. 1860. WINTERGREEN. Scape 15 cm high or less; leaves glaucous, 3.5 cm long or less, oblanceolate, entire.

Occasional on east slopes of Cascades in dry open woods. C and AT. Black Crater trail at 1525 m (5000 ft)); east slope McKenzie Pass 1250 m (4100 ft).

Pyrola minor L. Sp. Pl. 1:396. 1753. COMMON WINTERGREEN. Scape 10-20 cm high; leaves suborbicular, 2.5 cm long or less, obscurely crenate.

Infrequent in moist woods. Mostly C. West Lava Camp; Trout Cr. Swamp 1350 m (4450 ft); Three Creek L.

Pyrola secunda L. Sp. Pl. 1:396. 1753 (*Ramischia secunda* (L. Garke.). ONE-SIDED WINTERGREEN.

Scape 7:5-15 cm high; leaves ovate, crenulate, 1.5-3.5 cm long .

Common in woods. H. and C. Lake Valley; Frog Camp; Trout Cr. road at 1280 m (4200 ft); Little Brother 2285 m (7500 ft); Green Lakes region 2285 m (7500 ft); Sunshine Shelter.

RHODODENDRON L.

Rhododendron albiflorum Hook. Fl. Bor. Am. 2:43. 1843. WHITE-FLOWERED RHODODENDRON. Erect branching shrub with exfoliating bark, 1-1.5 m high; leaves deciduous, 3.5-5 cm long, elliptic, with scattered rusty pubescense, mostly entire, flowers cream-white, in few-flowered axillary clusters; stamens 10.

Rare in area. Lower H. Wooded border of Scott L.

VACCINIUM L. Huckleberry

Calyx deeply 4-5-lobed, the triangular lobes persistent; flowers
    solitary or in clusters of 2-3; leaves entire ....*V. occidentale*

Calyx shallowly lobed, the rounde dlobes deciduous;
    flowers solitary in the leaf axils
    Berries 4 mm in diameter, bright red; low much-branched
      shrub, the branches slender, green, strongly angled;
      leaves oval, about 9 mm long ....*V. scoparium*

    Berries larger, dark red, blue or black, with or without a bloom;
      branches not slender nor strongly angled; leaves broader
    Plant usually 30 cm or less high; leaves serrate above the middle;
      branches terete or slightly angled
      Corolla twice as long as broad; filaments longer than the
        anthers; berries dark blue with a bloom ....*V. caespitosum*

      Corolla nearly globose; filaments shorter than the anthers;
      berries dark blue with a bloom ....*V. deliciosum*

    Plant well above 30 cm high; leaves entire or serrate;
      branches slightly angled
    Leaves sharply serrate; berries dark purplish-red
      to black, without a bloom ....*V. membranaceum*

    Leaves entire or slightly serrate below the middle;
      berries blue-black with a bloom ....*V. ovalifolium*

Vaccinium caespitosum Michx. Fl. Bor. Am. 1:234. 1803. DWARF HUCKLEBERRY. Low rigid shrub; leaves thin, oblanceolate, 1.2-3.6 cm long, glabrous, serrulate, paler and glossy beneath, strongly reticulate; berries about 6 mm broad.

Frequent in moist ground. H to T. Lava Camp L.; Matthieu L.; Sparks L.; Green Lakes; Todd L.

Vaccinium deliciosum Piper, Mazama 2:103. 1901. BLUE-LEAVED HUCKLEBERRY. Low bushy shrub, glabrous; leaves obovate, 2.5-3.5 cm long, serrulate, pale green above, somewhat glaucous beneath; berries 6 mm or more broad.

Abundant in alpine meadows. H. Matthieu L.; Huckleberry L. trail 1585 m (5200 ft); Scott Mt. at 1740 m. (5700 ft); Benson L.; Melakwa L. trail 1515 m (4975 ft); White Branch Cr. 1800 m (5900 ft); Sunshine Shelter; Mirror L. 1830 m (6000 ft).

Vaccinium membranaceum Dougl. ex Hook. Fl. Bor. Amer. 2:32. 1834, as a synonym; Torr. Bot. Wilkes Exp. 377. 1878. THIN-LEAVED HUCKELBERRY. Slender branching shrub, 0.6-1.5 m high; leaves usually 2.5 cm or more long, glabrous, ovate, elliptical, or obovate, distinctly serrulate, usually acute at apex; berries 10 mm or more broad, dark purplish-red without bloom.

Common, usually abundant in open woods. H and C. Huckleberry L.; Lava Camp L.; Frog Camp; Scott Mt.; Sunshine Shelter; near Soda Spg. ca. 1980 m (6500 ft); Obsidian Cliffs.

Vaccinium occidentale Gray, Bot. Calif. 1:451. 1876. WESTERN HUCKLEBERRY. Low much-branched shrub, branches not angled; leaves mostly less than 1.8 cm long, obovate to oblanceolate, entire, glaucous; berries about 6 mm broad, blue-black with a bloom.

Frequent in bogs and wet meadows. H and C. Lake Valley; Huckleberry L.; Green Lakes; Todd L.; Three Creek L.

Vaccinium ovalifolium Smith in Rees, Cycl. 36: no. 2. 1817. OVAL-LEAVED HUCKLEBERRY. Shrub, 0.3-1.0 m or more high; branches angled; leaves 3.5 cm or less long, oval, entire, glabrous; berries blue-black with bloom, ca 1 cm broad.

Infrequent in woods. Lower H and C. Spring L.; West Lava Camp.

Vaccinium scoparium Leiberg, Mazama 1:196. 1897. SMALL LEAVED HUCKLEBERRY. Low tufted shrub with many slender broom-like branches, sharply angled, glabrous; leaves narrowly ovate, about 12 mm or less long, serrulate; berries ca 5 mm broad, bright red.

Common in woods. H and C. Frog Camp; Hand L.; Sand Spg.; Sunshine Shelter at 2255 m (7400 ft); Green Lakes; Todd L.; Middle Sister above timberline.

44. PRIMULACEAE　Primrose Family

DODECATHEON L.

Dodecatheon jeffreyi Van Houtte, Fl. de Serres 16:99. pl. 1682. 1865. TALL MOUNTAIN SHOOTING STAR. Perennial herb, glandular-puberulent above; leaves oblanceolate to oblong, tapering at base, 8-15 cm long, entire or remotely denticulate, basal; scape 20 or more cm high; umbels commonly many-flowered; calyx 5-cleft, the lobes minutely puberulent, strongly reflexed; corolla 5-lobed, rose-pink, strongly reflexed; stamens 5, opposite the corolla-lobes, reddish-purple; capsule ovoid, transversely dehiscent, many-seeded.

Frequent in moist meadows. H. Lake Valley; Frog Camp; Sunshine Shelter, south at 1980 m (6500 ft); Todd L.; Green Lakes.

45. GENTIANACEAE　Gentian Family

Perennial herbs; leaves opposite, simple, entire; calyx persistent; corolla funnelform to rotate; sta-mens as many as the corolla-lobes and alternate with them; ovary 1-celled.

GENTIANA L.

Gentiana newberryi Gray, Proc. Amer. Acad. 11:84. 1876. NEWBERRY'S GENTIAN. Leaves glabrous, spatulate, the cauline smaller, sessile; stems 1-several, 6-10 cm high, 1-flowered; calyx-lobes about equaling the tube; corolla deep blue, whitish and green dotted within, narrowly-funnelform, plaited; capsule ovoid; seeds broadly winged.

Occasional in meadows. H. Lake Valley; east of Broken Top 2135 m (7000 ft); Three Creek L.

46. MENYANTHACEAE　Buckbean Family

MENYANTHES L.

Menyanthes trifoliata L. Sp. Pl. 1:145. 1753. BUCKBEAN. Perennial aquatic herb, glabrous; creeping rootstock; leaves alternate, basal, trifoliate, the leaflets obovate or narrower and sessile; petioles 15-25 cm long, dilated and sheathing at the base; raceme borne on long naked peduncle arising from the rootstock; flowers 15-20, white, bearded within; capsule ovoid, about 8 mm long.

Infrequent. H and lower. Sparks L., slough, in 30 to 60 cm of water; Trout Cr. Swamp.

47. APOCYNACEAE　Dogbane Family

Herbs or shrubs with milky juice; leaves mostly opposite.

APOCYNUM L.

Perennial herbs; leaves opposite, entire; stamens attached to base of corolla-tube and alternating with 5 small appendages; fruit a pair of slender follicles; seeds many, with long coma.

Apocynum pumilum (Gray) Greene, Man. Bay Reg. 240. 1894. DWARF DOGBANE. Plant 15-20 cm high, glabrous, much branched; leaves drooping, ovate to oblong-lanceolate, petioled; cymes terminal and from the upper leaf-axils; calyx-lobes broadly ovate; corolla 4-6 mm long, pink-tinged, tube cylindric, lobes recurved in age; follicles erect, divergent, about 6 cm long.

Infrequent. Lower dry sandy slopes. Lower H to AT. Pine Butte.

48. POLEMONIACEAE　Phlox Family

Herbs or small shrubs; leaves simple or compound; corolla 5-merous, united; calyx united, 5-lobed.

A *Gentiana newberryi*; B *Phlox diffusa*; C *Apocynum pumilum*; D *Collomia larsenii*;
E *Menyanthes trifoliata*

KEY TO THE GENERA OF POLEMONICEAE

Calyx not distended nor burst by the capsule
  Calyx partly scarious, sinuses distended into a revolute lobe,
    leaves lobed or parted, corolla narrowly funnelform ....*Collomia*

  Calyx entirely herbaceous, sinuses not distended,
    leaves pinnately compound, corolla rotate ....*Polemonium*

Calyx distended and burst by the growing capsule
  Leaves opposite, entire; corolla salverform
    Annual, corolla small ....*Microsteris*

    Perennial, corolla large ....*Phlox*

  Leaves alternate, usually not entire;
    corolla tubular, funnelform or salverform ....*Gilia*

COLLOMIA Nutt.

Collomia larsenii (Gray) Payson Univ. Wyo. Pub. Sci. 1:85. 1924. TALUS COLLOMIA. Perennial herb 5-10 cm high; stems branched, decumbent; rootstock deep-seated, slender; leaves much dissected, thinly villous; flowers crowded at ends of branches; calyx hairy, 6-7 mm long, the lobes acute, about equaling the tube; corolla purple, twice the length of the calyx, the slender tube dilated to the throat; stamens 5, unequal, inserted at base of throat and alternate with corolla lobes, exserted; capsule obo-void, cells 1-seeded.

Frequent on highest peaks well above timber-line in loose volcanic rocks. A. Black Crater 2215 m (7260 ft); Little Brother 2385 m (7820 ft); North and Middle Sister; Broken Top above 2440 m (8000 ft).

GILA Ruiz. & Pav.

Perennial or biennial; leaves mostly alternate, entire or variously lobed; inflorescence mostly panic-ulate or congested.

KEY TO THE SPECIES OF GILIA

Corolla red, about 25 mm long ....*G. aggregata*

Corolla white, about 6 mm long ....*G. congesta*

Gilia aggregata (Pursh) Spreng. Syst. 1:626. 1825. SCARLET GILIA. Biennial; stems simple, 30-90 cm high; leaves deeply pinnatifid, the segments nar-row, remote, tomentose; inflorescence glandular, long, narrow; corolla tubular-funnelform, 25 mm or more long, bright red; capsule ovoid, about equaling the calyx; seeds many in each of the 3 cells.

Barely enter sarea on eastern slopes at lower ele-vations. AT. East of McKenzie Pass at 1280 m (4200 ft); south of Black Pine Spring at 1770 m (5800 ft).

Gilia congesta Hook. Fl. Bor. Amer. 2:75. 1838. MANY-FLOWERED GILIA. Perennial; stems several from branching caudex, 12-15 cm high, loosely tomentose; leaves pinnately parted; flowers in heads; flowers salverform, white, the corolla 4-6 mm long; capsule obovoid, shorter than the calyx.

Rare. A. Broken Top above 2440 m (8000 ft).

MICROSTERIS Greene

Microsteris gracilis (Dougl.) Greene, Pittonia 3:300. 1898. SLENDER PHLOX. Annual, 2.5-15 cm. high, simple or with spreading branches, glandular; corolla light purple to white, small, the tube about 12 mm long, ribbed; seeds mucilaginous when wet.

Infrequent in dry to moist sandy soil. Lower H to T. West Lava Camp; Linton Cr., springs 1860 m (6100 ft).

PHLOX L.

Phlox diffusa Benth. Pl. Hartw. 325. 1849. SPREADING PHLOX. Low perennial herb, woody base, spreading or prostrate forming mats; leaves linear, entire, mostly glabrate, somewhat sharp-pointed; calyx 5-lobed, ribbed, arachnoid-tomentose; corolla pinkish or light purple to white, 5-lobed, the tube about 1 2mm long; stamens 5, short, included.

Infrequent in dry open places. H and C. Scott L.; Scott Mt.

POLEMONIUM L.

Perennial herbs; leaves alternate, pinnately com-pound; calyx 5-lobed; corolla deeply 5-lobed; ovary 3-celled.

KEY TO THE SPECIES OF POLEMONIUM

Corolla-lobes twice the length of the tube,
    leaflets 1-2.5 cm long, lanceolate or oblong, acute ....*P. californicum*

Corolla-lobes about equaling the tube,
    leaflets 4-7 mm long, 3-5 mm wide, ovate to round, obtuse ....*P. pulcherrimum*

Polemonium californicum Eastw. Bot. Gaz. 37:437. 1904. LOW POLEMONIUM. Perennial, 10-25 cm high; stems solitary or few; leaflets 6-10 pairs, the 3 terminal leaflets more or less confluent; corolla companulate, rotate, light blue; staments inserted about the mid-point of the corolla-tube, hairy at the base.

Occasional in dry woods. H. Middle Sister; Rock Mesa 2045 m (6700 ft); Linton Meadows 1860 m (6100 ft); Sparks L.; Todd L.

Polemonium pulcherrimum Hook. Bot. Mag. 57:2979. 1829. SHOWY POLEMONIUM. Perennial, 7.5-10 cm high; leaflets 6-10 pairs, obtuse; corolla

rotate-companulate, lobes about 5 mm long, light blue, the tube yellow; staments inserted below the middle of the tube, hairy at the base.

Common in sandy soil usually from well above timberline to the summit. A. Middle Sister at 3050 m (10,000 ft); South Sister at 2900 m (9500 ft); Black Crater 2210 m (7200 ft).

49. HYDROPHYLLACEAE   Waterleaf Family

Herbs or low shrubs, leaves mostly alternate, calyx 5-lobed, corolla 5-lobed, stamens 5 on the corolla tube, ovary superior, capsule 1 or 2-celled, seeds pitted.

A *Polemonium californicum;* **B** *Polemonium pulcherriumum*
C *Hydrophyllum fendleri albifrons*

KEY TO THE GENERA OF HYDROPHYLLACEAE

Flowers in head-like clusters, stamens and style long exserted ....*Hydrophyllum*

Flowers in more or less scorpioid cymes,
　　stamens and styles exserted or included..*Phacelia*

HYDROPHYLLUM L.

Perennial herbs with succulent tender stems, leaves pinnately divided, calyx divided almost to the base, corolla longer than the calyx, capsule 2-valved.

Hydrophyllum fendleri Heller var. **albifrons** Macbride, Contr. Gray Herb. No. 49:23. 1917. FENDLER WATERLEAF. Plant about 35 cm high, soft pubescent; leaves 8-15 cm long, long-petioled, 5-9-parted or divided, the segments deeply lobed or clerft, strigose above, more densely so and paler beneath; corolla light blue or lavender, about 1 cm long; filaments hairy.

Infrequent in woods near streams. H to T. Linton Meadows 1860 m (6100 ft); Soda Cr.

PHACELIA Juss.

Perennial or biennial herbs harshly pubescent; stamens exserted; style 2-cleft; flowers mostly 5-merous.

KEY TO THE SPECIES OF PHACELIA

Perennial, low, cespitose, with woody branching caudex;
　　leaves gray-green, hispid, elliptical, entire ....*P. hastata var, compacta*

Biennial, 20-40 cm high, slender taproot;
　　leaves greenish, somewhat hispid with spreading hairs,
　　divided with a pair of segments below the large terminal one.................*P. mutabilis*

Phacelia hastata Dougl. var. **compacta** (Brand) Cronq. Vasc. Pl. Pacif. NW. 4:163. 1959. TIMBERLINE PHACELIA. Low alpine plant; leaves mostly basal, densely clustered; cauline leaves much smaller, entire, remote; all leaves with stiff appressed hairs on both surfaces except along the veins on the upper surfaces causing the veins to appear deeply depressed; corolla pale lavender to whitish; stamens 6-8 mm long with glabrate filaments; capsule ovoid, acute, hispid.

Occasional on higher sandy slopes. A and H. Pine Butte; Little Brother; South Sister above 2745 m (9000 ft); Broken Top.

Phacelia mutabilis Greene, Erythea 4:55. 1896. CHANGEABLE PHACELIA. Biennial or weakly perennial; stems several, slender, ascending; leaves basal and cauline, lanceolate or broader, veins not very conspicuous, blades 2-6 cm or more in length; petioles slender, usually longer than the blades; flowers many, the clusters both terminal and from the leaf-axils; calyx-lobes linear; corolla lavender to dingy-white; stamens 6-8 mm long with hairy filaments; capsule ovoid, acute.

Infrequent in dry open woods. H to T. Trout Cr. Swamp; Scott Mt.; Wickiup Plain 1920 m (6300 ft); Soda Cr.

50. BORAGINACEAE　Borage Family

Herbs with alternate, entire leaves; flowers in scorpioid spikes or racemes; calyx 5-clerft; corolla gamopetalous, sometimes with appendages in the throat; stamens 5, inserted on the corolla-tube; ovary superior, of two 2-ovuled carpels, usually deeply lobed.

KEY TO THE GENERA OF BORAGINACEAE

Corolla white, sometimes light blue
　　Low annual ....*Allocarya*

　　Tall perennial or biennial ....*Hackelia*

Corolla deep blue ....*Cynglossum*

ALLOCARYA Green

Allocarya hispidula Greene, Pittonia 1:17. 1887. HARSH ALLOCARYA. Low annual; stems branched at base, prostrate or ascending, 6-30 cm long, strigose; leaves linear, strigose; racemens becoming elongated, loose; calyx densely setose; corolla 1-2 mm broad; nutlets 4, 1.5-2 mm long, long-ovate, hispidulous, wrinkled, ridged.

Rare in area, on eastern side. C and AT. Trout Cr. Swamp.

CYNOGLOSSUM L.

Cynoglossum occidentale Gray, Proc. Amer. Acad. 10:58. 1874. WESTERN HOUND'S TONGUE. Perennial; stems stout, leafy, 45 cm or more high, stiff-hairy; leaves narrowly oblanceolate, 10-20 cm long, on long winged petioles; corolla blue, often pink-tinged; nutlets 4, widely spreading, densely covered with barb-tipped spines.

Rare. AT. Trout Cr. road.

HACKELIA Opiz.

Perennial or biennial herbs; stems rather tall, leafy; leaves narrow, oblong; panicle naked or with bracts at the branches; calyx 5-parted; corolla blue, white or pinkish, the throat crested; nutlets 4 with barbed bristles.

KEY TO THE SPECIES OF HACKELIA

Corolla white, the backs of the nutlets with bristles
  about as long as those of the margins ....*H. californica*

Corolla white or blue, the backs of the nutlets with bristles
  shorter than those of the margins ....*H. diffusa*

Hackelia californica (Piper) Johnst. Contr. Gray Herb. No. 68:47. 1923. CALIFORNIA STICKSEED. Perennial, 30-45 cm high or higher; stems leafy, hairy; the lower leaves oblanceolate to oblong, the base narrowed to petiole about as long, the upper leaves smaller, sessile; inflorescence widely branched in age; flowers scattered, corolla all white.

Infreqent, east of crest in dry open woods. H to AT. Black Crater; Trout Cr. Butte.

Hackelia diffusa (Lehm.) Johnst. Contr. Gray Herb. No. 18:48. 1923. DIFFUSE STICKSEED. Perennial, 45-60 cm high, hirsute; leaves pubescent, the blades up to 15 cm long, narrowed into a long petiole, the upper stem-leaves reduced and becoming sessile; inflorescence, open peduncles long, leafy-bracted; corolla white, the tube shorter than the calyx.

Rare in area on eastern side, on open rocky slopes. Lower H to AT. Soda Cr. at 1725 m (5650 ft).

51. LABIATAE Mint Family

Herbs, usually aromatic; stems 4-sided; leaves opposite, simple; flowers irregular.

PRUNELLA L.

Prunella vulgaris L. Sp. Pl: 2:600: 1753. HEAL-ALL. Perennial, 15 or more cm high; stems loosely villous; flowers violet in dense terminal spikes and with large purplish bracts; corolla 2-lipped, contracted at the throat.

Infrequent in moist meadows. Lower H to HT. Pole Bridge 1465 m (4800 ft).

52. SCROPHULARICEAE Figwort Family

Perennial or annual herbs; leaves alternate or opposite; flowers mostly irregular; stamens 2 or 4; fruit a capsule; seeds many.

KEY TO THE GENERA OF SCROPHULARIACEAE

Leaves alternate
  Floral bracts large, brightly colored; flowers less showy
    Annual, flowers and tips of bracts purple ....*Orthocarpus*
    Perennial, floral bracts tipped bright red or purplish-red ....*Castilleja*
  Floral bracts smaller, greenish; flowers showy ....*Pedicularis*
Leaves opposite
  Fertile stamens 4, corolla bilabiate, calyx 5-lobed
    Calyx angled, no sterile stamen ....*Mimulus*

Calyx not angled

    Sterile stamen conspicuous, a long filament; perennial ....*Penstemon*

    Sterile stamen vestigial; annual...*Collinsia*

Fertile stamens 2, corolla rotate, calyx 4-lobed ....*Veronica*

CASTILLEJA Mutis   Indian Paint-brush

Perennial herbs; leaves alternate, often cleft, sessile; flowers in terminal spikes, subtended by leafy, often brightly colored bracts; calyx 4-cleft; corolla tubular, strongly bilabiate, the upper lip (galea) long and narrow, the lobes united to the tip and enclosing the anthers, the lower lip shorter, 3-lobed; stamens 4 unequal; seeds numerous.

KEY TO THE SPECIES OF CASTILLEJA

Bracts and calyx-tips scarlet or purple-red
  Bracts and calyx-tips scarlet
    Stems usually solitary, bracts with yellow band below scarlet tip ....*C. suksdorfii*

    Stems few, clustered, simple or branched; inflorescence bright red ....*C. miniata*

  Bracts and calyx-tips deep purplish-red ....*C. oreopola*

Bracts and calyx-tips greenish-yellow to orange .... *C. arachnoidea*

Castilleja arachnoidea Greenm. Bot. Gaz. 53: 510. 1912. COTTON PAINT-BRUSH. Perennial, stems clustered, 8-15 cm high, soft-woolly pubescent; leaves less hairy, linear-lanceolate with one or two pairs of very narrow, spreading lobes; bracts yellow-orange; corolla 8-10 mm long, the galea 3-4 mm long, woolly-pubescent on the dorsal side; capsule about 8 mm long.

Occasional on higher sandy slopes. H. Sunshine Shelter area 2290 m (7500 ft); Camp Riley; Green Lakes.

Castilleja miniata Dougl. ex Hooker Fl. Bor. Am. 2:106. 1838. COMMON PAINT-BRUSH. Perennial, 30-60 cm high; stems glabrous, or glabrate below the inflorescence; leaves glabrous, narrowly lanceolate or wider, acute, entire, the upper occasionally with a pair of short lobes; inflorescence pubescent; calyx cleft, the lobes lanceolate, scarlet; bracts red, usually with a pair of narrow lobes.

Occasional in meadows and open woods. H. Sparks L.; Todd L.; Three Cr., meadow 1920 m (6300 ft); Spring L.

Castilleja oreopola Greene, Bot. Gaz. 25:264. 1898. ROSY PAINT-BRUSH. Perennial, 15-50 cm high; stems clustered, mostly glabrous below the inflorescence; leaves lanceolate, with 1-2 pairs of narrow attenuate lobes, usually glabrous, 2-3 cm long; bracts and calyces rose to purplish-red; calyx about 20 mm long; inflorescence hairy, minutely glandular; capsule 11 mm long.

Common in open woods and meadows near timberline. A and H. Black Crater; Scott Mt.; Frog Camp; Middle Sister, west slope at 2290 m (7500 ft); Camp Agoseris; Green Lakes.

Castilleja suksdorfii Gray, Proc. Am. Acad. 22:311. 1887. SUKSDORF'S PAINT-BRUSH. Perennial; stems solitary or few from slender branching rootstock, 30-60 cm high, glabrate; leaves narrowly lanceolate, mostly entire or the upper with a pair of narrow lobes, 5-7 cm long; inflorescence villous, the spike dense, becoming loose; bracts scarlet above, greenish below with a yellow band between; calyx 2.5-3 cm long, cleft more than half way, the teeth very narrow; capsule about 12 mm long.

Occasional in meadows. H. West Lava Camp; Frog Camp; White Branch Cr. at 1800 m (5900 ft); Linton Meadows 1830 m (6000 ft); Sparks L.

COLLINSIA Nutt.

Collinsia parviflora Dougl. ex Lindl. Bot. Reg. 13: pl. 1082. 1827. SMALL-FLOWERED COLLINSIA. Annual with slender, weak stems, 5-25 cm high, puberulent; upper leaves opposite, ovate, narrow, entire or with few teeth, 2.5 cm or more long, petioled; inflorescence lax, each one or two flowers subtended by a bract, pedicels slender, long; calyx 5-cleft; corolla strongly bilabiate, 4-8 mm long, glabrous; upper lip white, blue distally; lower lip with blue lateral lobes; corolla-tube white; capsule 4 mm long.

Rare. H. Usually C and HT. Rocky slope, Soda Cr. at 1735 m (5700 ft).

MIMULUS L.

Annual or perennial herbs; leaves opposite; calyx strongly 5-angled, 5-toothed; corolla more or less bilabiate, yellow or red; stamens 4, stigma 2-lobed.

A *Phacelia hastata compacta;* **B** *Pedicularis racemosa;* **C** *Mimulus guttatus;*
D *Hackelia californica;* **E** *Pedicularis attolens;* **F** *Castilleja suksdorfii*

KEY TO THE SPECIES OF MIMULUS

Corolla yellow
  Calyx nearly regular, lobes about equal
    Calyx-lobes ⅓ to ½ as long as the tube; stems branched, leafy ....*M. moschatus*

    Calyx-lobes less than ⅓ as long as the tube;
      leaves crowded near base of stem ....*M. primuloides*

  Calyx quite irregular, upper lobe longest
    Flowers few, 1-5 terminal or axillary;
      rhizome creeping; alpine plant..*M. tilingii*

    Flowers more numerous; rhizome rarely creeping;
      low to moderate elevations ....*M. guttatus*

Corolla red
  Flowers small, slender; corolla less than twice as long as the calyx ....*M. breweri*

  Flowers large, showy; corolla at least twice as long as the calyx ....*M. lewisii*

Mimulus breweri (Greene) Coville, Contr. U.S. Nat. Herb. 4:171. 1893. BREWER'S MONKEY-FLOWER. Low annual, slender, simple or branched, glandular-pubescent; leaves opposite, linear to linear-elliptic; corolla purple-red; calyx reddish.

Occasional in damp sandy soil. H to T. Obsidian Falls 1980 m (6500 ft); Soda Cr., upper; Hand L.

Mimulus guttatus Fischer ex DC. Cat. Hort. Monsp. 127. 1813. COMMON MONKEY-FLOWER. Annual, or sometimes perennial by rootstocks, 15-30 cm high; leaves ovate to round, dentate, glabrous; corolla 2.5 cm or more long, throat pubescent, more or less red-spotted, the lower lip much longer than the upper; anthers glabrous; stigmas fimbriolate; capsule stipitate, shorter than the calyx.

Frequent in wet ground. H to T. Hand L.; Goose Cr. at Sparks L.; Todd L.; Trout Cr. Swamp.

Mimulus lewisii Pursh, Fl. 2:427. pl. 20. 1814. LEWIS' MONKEY-FLOWER. Perennial, 15-75 cm high; viscid-pubescent; leaves lanceolate to ovate, shallowly dentate, acute, sessile; calyx-lobes acuminate; corolla 3-4.5 cm long, purplish-red or rose-pink, the throat villous; anthers villous; capsule shorter than the calyx.

Occasional on wet stream banks. H and C. McKenzie Pass; White Branch Cr.; Linton Meadows; Mesa Cr.; Green Lakes.

Mimulus moschatus Dougl. ex Lindl. Bot. Reg. 13: pl. 1118. 1828. MUSK MONKEY-FLOWER. Perennial, glandular-pilose, somewhat slimy and with musky odor; stems weak, decumbent or diffuse, 10-25 cm long; corolla pale yellow, throat narrow, with stripes and dots; capsule shorter than the calyx.

Infrequent in wet places. Lower H to T. Pole Bridge.

Mimulus primuloides Benth. Scroph. Ind. 29. 1935. PRIMROSE MONKEY-FLOWER. Perennial, often matted, 3-6 cm high; leaves crowded near base, broadly oblanceolate, villous on one or both sides, or glabrous; flowers mostly solitary on a slender peduncle; corolla yellow, 12-18 mm long; throat dilated, funnelform.

Frequent in damp meadows. H to T. Lake Valley; Frog Camp; Three Cr. at about 2135 m (7000 ft); Trout Cr. Swamp.

Mimulus tilingii Regel, Gartenfl. 18:321. pl. 631. 1869. MOUNTAIN MONKEY-FLOWER. Perennial with creeping rhizomes; stems simple or branched, 8-30 cm high, slender, glabrous or pubescent; leaves mostly ovate, dentate; corolla yellow, mottled, 1.5-3 cm long; upper lip shorter, with two ascending lobes, lower lip longer, with three deflexed-spreading lobes; capsule short-stipitate, 7-8 mm long.

Frequent, wet stream banks and lake shores. H. Frog Camp; Spring L.; Linton Meadows; Green Lakes; Three Creek L.

ORTHOCARPUS Nutt.

Orthocarpus imbricatus Torr. ex Wats. Bot. King Explor. 458. 1871. MOUNTAIN ORTHOCARPUS. Annual, 15-35 cm high, branched above; inflorescence, dense spikes at the ends of the branches; leaves linear-lanceolate, entire, scabrous, about 4-5 cm long; bracts broadly oblong, puberulent, purple-tipped; corolla purple, about 12 mm long, little dilated.

Rare in open woods. H and C. Deer Butte Prairie.

PEDICULARIS L.

Perennial herbs; leaves alternate, toothed or bipinnatifid, often basal; flowers in terminal racemes or spikes; calyx irregularly lobed; corolla 2-lipped; stamens 4 of unequal lengths; capsule flattened; seeds several.

KEY TO THE SPECIES OF PEDICULARIS

Leaves doubly toothed, lower flowers axillary ....*P. racemosa*

Leaves bipinnatifid, none of the flowers axillary
   Flowers reddish purple
      Inflorescence glabrous, beak of upper lip of corolla 12 mm long ....*P. groenlandica*

      Inflorescence villous, beak about 5 mm long ....*P. attolens*

   Flowers greenish-yellow ....*P. flavida*

Pedicularis attolens Gray, Proc. Amer. Acad. 7:384. 1867. LITTLE ELEPHANT'S HEAD. Stems one or few from short rootstock, 15-30 cm or more high; leaves pinnately-divided into 12 or more pairs of narrow sharply-toothed pinnules; spike about 10 cm long or more; bracts equaling or shorter than the flowers, lobed; corolla about 7 mm long, the upper lip strongly arched, long beaked, reddish-purple.

Frequent in meadows. H to C. Ball Butte 2165 m (7150 ft); Green Lakes; Devil's Garden Camp.

Pedicularis flavida Penn. Bull. Torrey Club 61:445. 1934. CASCADE MOUNTAINS LOUSEWORT. Glabrous perennial, 30-60 cm or more high; leaves 7-10 cm long, divided into several pairs of pinnules, each doubly lobed or toothed; bracts of the spike-like raceme shorter than the flowers; calyx 5-lobed, the lobes attenuate; corolla 15 mm or more long, pale greenish-yellow, the galea strongly hooded with rounded apex, lower lip shorter, the lobes spreading; capsule 9 mm long, apex decurved.

Occasional in meadows. H to C. Obsidian Trail southeast of Frog Camp 1620 m (5300 ft); Three Cr.

Pedicularis groenlandica Retz. var. **surrecta** (Benth.) Piper, Mazama 2:100. 1901. ELEPHANT'S HEAD. Perennial, glabrous, 30-60 cm high; leaves lanceolate in outline with 12 or more pairs of pinnules cut to the midrib and serrate-dentate; bracts of the inflorescence shorter than the flowers, with several pairs of slender lobes; calyx 5-lobed; corolla red-purple, beak of galea 8-14 mm long, its hood and lower lip pale; anther cells acute; capsule about 8 or 10 mm long.

Frequent in wet meadows. H. Frog Camp; Devil's Garden Camp.

Pedicularis racemosa Dougl. Hook. Fl. Bor. Am. 2:108. 1838. LEAFY LOUSEWORT. Perennial, loosely tufted, 20-35 cm high, glabrous below the inflorescence; leaves all cauline, lanceolate, about 5 cm long, doubly serrate; bracts of the inflorescence equaling or longer than the flowers; corolla 10-12 mm long, rose-pink; the lower lip very broad, lobed; the upper lip erect, widening to form the hood, then abruptly decurved and narrowed to form the beak which is also strongly decurved; capsule 10 mm long or longer.

Occasional in open woods. H to C. Frog Camp; Middle Sister; Linton Meadows at 1860 m (6100 ft).

PENSTEMON Mitch.

Perennial herbs; leaves opposite; flowers mostly large, showy; calyx 5-parted; corolla long, bilabiate, the upper lip 2-lobed, the lower 3-lobed; fertile stamens 4, paired; sterile stamen 1, consisting of filament only.

KEY TO THE SPECIES OF PENSTEMON

Anthers densely long-wolly
   Inflorescence simple, glandular or slightly so,
      corolla glabrous externally
      Ascending or erect, not forming mats
         Leaves lanceolate, acute, toothed or entire ....*P. fruticosus*

         Leaves elliptic, obtuse, serrulate ....*P. cardwellii*

   Prostrate, forming mats
      Corolla blue-lavender, leaves glabrous not glaucous,
         sterile stamen bearded ....*P. davidsonii*

Corolla rose-purple, leaves puberulent, glaucous,
  sterile stamen glabrous or sparsely bearded ....*P. rupicola*

Inflorescence compound, strongly glandular,
  corolla glandular externally ....*P. nemorosus*

Anthers glabrous or nearly so
  Foliage strongly glaucous, anther sacs longer than wide ....*P. euglaucus*

Foliage not strongly glaucous, anther sacs not longer than wide
  Leaves narrowly lanceolate to linear,
    calyx lobes with broad scarious margin ....*P. cinicola*

Leaves wider, calyx lobes with narrow scarious margin ....*P. procerus*

Penstemon cardwellii Howell, Fl. N.W. Amer. 510. 1901. CARDWELL'S PENSTEMON. Low shrub, 12-24 cm high, spreading, puberulent; leaves elliptic, remotely serrate; corolla bright purple, 2.5 cm or more long.

Occasional in open woods. H to T. Melakwa L.; Tenas Lakes; Scott Mt.

Penstemon cinicola Keck, Carnegie Inst, Wash. Publ. 520:294. 1940. ASH PENSTEMON. Tufted, nearly glabrous, 15-30 cm high; leaves linear-lanceolate, 2.5-5 cm long; corolla 5-8 mm long, purplish-blue; sterile stamen included, hairy at the tip.

Rare, east of the divide in dry sandy soil. H to mostly AT. Ball Butte, base at about 2135 m (7000 ft).

Penstemon davidsonii Greene, Pittonia 2:241. 1892. CREEPING PENSTEMON. Low shrubby plants, creeping, freely branched, forming broad dense mats; leaves small, oval or spatulate; corolla 2 cm or more long.

Common in lava beds and on rocky slopes. A and H. McKenzie Pass; Windy Point; Black Crater, summit; Little Belnap Crater 1920 m (6300 ft); Middle Sister; South Sister, near Rock Mesa 2135 m (7000 ft); Ball Butte, summit 2470 m (8100 ft).

Penstemon euglaucus English, Proc. Biol. Soc. Wash. 41:197. 1928. GLAUCOUS PENSTEMON. Glabrous and glaucous throughout; stems slender, 20-60 cm high; leaves lanceolate, 4-6 cm long; inflorescence of widely separated clusters, the lower on peduncles, one from each leaf-axil; flowers 1 cm long or longer; corolla purple, blue, sometimes pinkish.

Common in dry sandy soil. Lower H to AT. McKenzie Pass; Scott Mt.; Trout Cr. Butte; Black Pine Spring 1290 m (4234 ft).

Penstemon fruticosus (Pursh) Greene, Pittonia 2:239. 1892. SHRUBBY PENSTEMON. Shrubby at base, spreading, forming clumps, 10-35 cm high; inflores-

cence a simple raceme; flowers about 2.5 cm long; corolla light purple-blue, serile stamen slender, yellow-bearded, half as long as the fertile filaments.

Infrequent in open woods. Lower H to AT. Tenas Lakes; Trout Cr. Butte.

Penstemon nemorosus (Dougl.) Trautv., Bull. Acad. St. Petersb. 5:345. 1839. WOODLAND PENSTEMON. Stems few, erect, 30-60 cm high, puberulent; leaves all cauline, broadly lanceolate, 5-10 cm long, sharply dentate, short-petioled; corolla 2.5 cm long, reddish-purple; sterile stamen slender, bearded.

Frequent in open woods. H to T. McKenzie Pass; Lava Camp L.; Sunshine Shelter; Sparks L.

Penstemon procerus var. **brachyanthus** (Pennell) Cronq. Vas. Pl. Pac. NW. 4:398. 1959. SHORT-FLOWERED PENSTEMON. Tufted plants, 10-25 cm high, leafy, decumbent below, puberulent; inflorescence of 2 or more whorl-like clusters; corolla light blue-purple, 1 cm long, glabrous without, the palate thinly pubescent; sterile stamen bearded.

Common in dry open woods. H. Frog Camp; Sunshine Shelter; Camp Riley; Rock Mesa area 2000 m (6575 ft); Green Lakes.

Penstemon rupicola Howell, Fl. N. W. Amer. 510. 1901. ROCK PENSTEMON. Shrubby, low, matted; leaves 1-2 cm long, ovate to nearly orbicular, irregularly serrate, thick, glaucous, usually glabrous; corolla rose-purple, 1 cm or more long; sterile stamen (staminode) shorter than the fertile, bearded.

Occasional in lava beds and rocky places. H. Tenas Lakes; North Sister; Linton Meadows 1860 m (6100 ft); Wickiup Plain; Soda Cr.

VERONICA L.

Perennial or annual herbs; leaves mostly opposite; flowers small; sepals 4, corolla 4-lobed; capsule flattened, notched at apex.

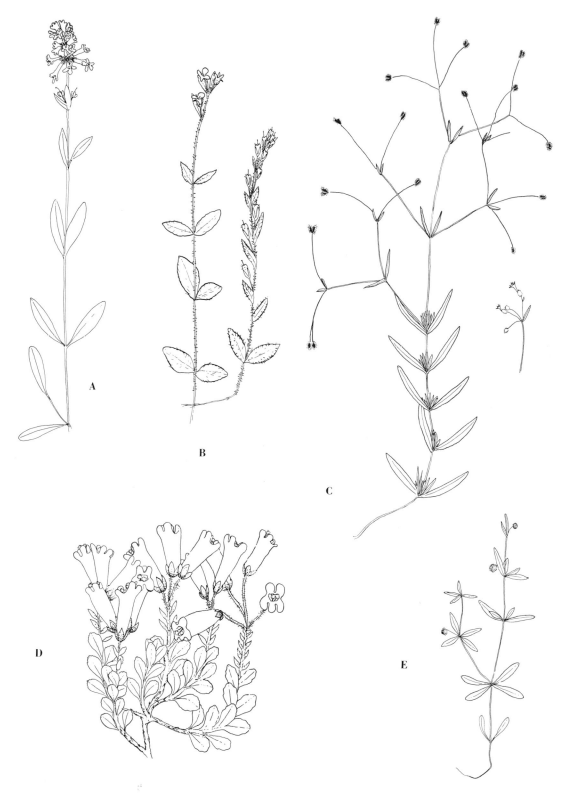

A *Penstemon procerus brachyanthus*; **B** *Veronica wormskjoldii*; **C** *Kelloggia galioides*;
D *Penstemon rupicola*; **E** *Galium bifolium*

Plant glabrous throughout; flowers in axillary racemes; leaves
    long-ovate to lanceolate; capsule orbicular, scarcely notched .... *V. americana*

Plant glandular-pubescent; flowers in terminal racemes or
    solitary in leaf-axils; leaves elliptic or ovate
    Capsule broader than long, deeply notched;
      corolla light blue with darker lines ....*V. serpyllifolia*

    Capsule longer than broad, broadly notched; corolla deep blue ....*V. wormskjoldii*

Veronica americana (Raf.) Schwein. ex Benth. in A. DC. Prod. 10:468. 1846. AMERICAN BROOK-LIME. Perennial, 15-45 cm high; leaves lanceolate, 3-4 times longer than broad, serrulate; corolla blue, about 0.5 cm broad.

Rare in area, wet places. H and C. Trout Cr. Swamp.

Veronica serpyllifolia L. Sp. Pl. 12. 1753. THYME-LEAVED SPEEDWELL. Perennial, decumbent at base, 10-25 cm high; leaves shallowly serrate; corolla light blue.

Infrequent in meadows. Naturalized from Eurasia. Lake Valley; Soda Cr.

Veronica wormskjoldii Roem. & Sch. Syst. Veg. 1:101. 1817. ALPINE SPEEDWELL. Perennial, 10-20 cm high; leaves mostly elliptic, 1-2.5 cm long, half as broad; corolla 7.5 mm or more broad, deep blue.

Common in moist meadows. H. McKenzie Pass; Lake Valley; Linton Meadows; Goose Cr.; the Husband.

53. LENTIBULARACEAE   Bladderwort Family

UTRICULARIA L.

Aquatic herbs, submersed; stems sparingly branched; leaves much dissected and bearing bouyant bladders.

Utricularia vulgaris L. Sp. Pl. 1:18. 1753. COM-MON BLADDERWORT. Submerged, often free-floating; stems 1 m or more long, little branched; calyx 2-lipped; corolla yellow, deeply bilabiate, the lower lip larger, about 1 cm broad, 3-lobed, spurred at base; stamens 2; ovary superior, 1-celled, bearing several ovules.

Infrequent in still water. H to T. Slough near Sparks L.

54. PLANTAGINACEAE   Plantain Family

PLANTAGO L.

Plantago major L. Sp. Pl. 1:113. 1753. COMMON PLANTAIN. Perennial herb; scapes erect, 20-25 cm high; leaves basal, ovate, entire or slightly toothed, 8-20 cm long on slender petioles; inflorescence a slender, dense, terminal spike of small flowers; calyx 4-parted; corolla 4-lobed, 1-1.5 mm long, reflexed, petals white; stemens 4, long-exserted; capsules transversely dehiscent, ovoid, 3 mm long; seeds 8-18.

Rare. Probably carried into camp site in horse feed. Naturalized from Europe. Scott L., camp.

55. RUBIACEAE   Madder Family

Herbs, shrubs or trees; leaves opposite or whorled; calyx-tube adnate to the ovary; corolla gamopetalous, 4-5-lobed; stamens 4-5 borne on the corolla, alternate with the lobes; fruit a capsule, berry, drupe, drupelet or nutlet.

Leaves whorled, corolla rotate ....*Galium*

Leaves opposite, corolla funnelform ....*Kelloggia*

GALIUM L.

Annual or perennial herbs; stems slender, 4-angled; leaves opposite or apparently whorled.

Annual, slender, erect, branched, glabrous, upper leaves opposite ....*G. bifolium*

Perennial
Leaves 4-6 in a whorl; flowers usually solitary, or 2-3 on
    axillary or terminal peduncles ....*G. trifidum* var. *pacificum*
Leaves 4 in a whorl; similar to above but lower, matted ....*G. brandegei*

Galium bifolium S. Wats. Bot. King Explor. 134. 1871. LOW MOUNTAIN BEDSTRAW. Plant 7-20 cm high; upper leaves opposite, the lower 4-whorled, unequal; flowers solitary in the axils.

Occasional in woods. H to C. Soda Cr., upper; Todd L.

Galium brandegei Gray, Proc. Am. Acad. 12:58. 1876. BRANDEGEE'S BEDSTRAW. Stems slender, 5-10 cm long, matted or ascending, somewhat scabrous on the angles; leaves in 4's, 5-8 mm long, oblanceolate, rounded at apex, the margins smooth or slightly roughened; corolla minute, white; fruit glabrous, minute.

Infrequent in moist places. Lower H and C. Frog Camp; Craig L.

Galium trifidum (L.) var. **pacificum** Wieg. Bull. Torrey Club 24:400. 1879. SMALL BEDSTRAW. Stems 20-60 cm long, slender, weak or ascending, branching, angles minutely roughened; leaves oblanceolate or narrower, obtuse, 1-2 cm long; corolla minute, white; fruit minute, glabrous.

Infrequent in marshy meadows. H and C. Pole Bridge; Trout Cr. Swamp.

KELLOGGIA Torr.

Kelloggia galioides Torr. Bot. Wilkes. Exped. 332. 1874. KELLOGGIA. Perennial herb, 15-30 cm or more high, slender; leaves opposite, lanceolate, 2.5-4 cm long, 0.3-1 cm wide, glabrous, entire, sessile; corolla pinkish or white; flowers small on long pedicels; fruit dry, oblong, 4-5 mm long, covered with short hooked bristles.

Occasional in dry open woods. H and C. Scott Mt., summit; Black Crater Tr. at 1420 m (4950 ft) ; east slope McKenzie Pass.

56. CAPRIFOLIACEAE Honeysuckle Family

Herbs or shrubs; leaves opposite, simple or pinnately compound; flowers perfect; calyx-tube adnate to the ovary; corolla tubular to rotate, mostly 5-lobed; stamens on the petals, mostly 5; fruit usually fleshy, indehiscent.

KEY TO THE GENERA OF CAPRIFOLIACEAE

Slender creeping herbs, flowers paired on slender peduncles ....*Linnaea*
Erect shrubs, flowers not paired on slender peduncles
    Leaves pinnately compound ....*Sambucus*
    Leaves simple
        Style short, 3-cleft, fruit 1-seeded ....*Viburnum*
        Style elongated, shrubs erect or twining
            Corolla regular, fruit berry-like, white, 2-seeded ....*Symphoricarpos*
        Corolla somewhat irregular, fruit a red or black berry ....*Lonicera*

LINNAEA L.

Linnaea borealis L. var. **americana** (Forbes) Rehder. Rhodora 6:56. 1904. TWINFLOWER. Perennial, stems woody, slender, long-creeping; leaves opposite, evergreen, 1-2 cm long, orbicular to obovate, toothed above the middle, glabrate, short-petioled; flowers pinkish, in pairs, erect on long peduncles; ovary glandular.

Rare in area. Common in woods at lower altitudes. C. Trout Cr. Swamp.

LONICERA L.

Shrubs, erect or twining; leaves opposite, deciduous, simple, entire; calyx-lobes 5, small; stamens 5, inserted on the corolla-tube; fruit a berry.

KEY TO THE SPECIES OF LONICERA

Flowers without involucre, corolla dark red ....*L. conjugialis*
Flowers in axillary pairs subtended by a pair of large bracts
    forming an involucre, corolla yellow ....*L. involucrata*

A *Sambucus callicarpa;* **B** *Lonicera involucrata;* **C** *Valeriana sitchensis*

Lonicera conjugialis Kellogg, Proc. Cal. Acad. 2:67. 1863. RED TWIN-BERRY. Deciduous shrub 60-150 cm high; leaves obovate to elliptic; corolla dark red; fruit a very dark red berry, the two carpels not completely fused.

Infrequent in open woods. Lower H to C. Craig L. 1555 m (5100 ft); Trout Cr. Butte, summit 1675 m (5500 ft).

Lonicera involucrata Banks, Richards Bot. App. Frankl. Journ. 733. 1823. BLACK TWIN-BERRY. Deciduous shrub, 1-2.5 m high; leaves obovate, ovate or elliptic, entire, acute; involucre large, dark red; corolla yellow, long-funnelform, 1-2 cm long; berries separate, globose, black.

Frequent along streams. Lower H to HT. Lake Valley; Frog Camp; McKenzie Pass; Sparks L.

SAMBUCUS L.

Sambucus callicarpa Greene, Fl. Fran. 342. 1892. RED ELDERBERRY. Deciduous shrub, 2-3 m or more high; leaves odd-pinnate; 5-7 leaflets, lanceolate to oblong-ovate, 6-15 cm long, sharply serrate to the apex; flowers white, borne in pyramidal panicles; berries bright red, about 4 mm in diameter.

Common about lava beds in damp soil. H to HT. West Lava Camp; McKenzie Pass; Sparks L.

SYMPHORICARPOS Duhamel

Symphoricarpos albus (L.) Blake, Rhodora 16:118. 1914. SNOWBERRY. Deciduous shrub, 60-120 cm high, much branched; leaves simple, entire or somewhate lobed, ovate to elliptic, 1.5-3 cm long, with scattered hairs beneath, short-petioled; flowers in terminal and axillary clusters; corolla campanulate, 5-6 mm long, pinkish-white, strongly villous within; fruit a white globose berry, 6-12 mm in diameter.

Infrequent in open woods. Common at lower altitudes. Lower H to HT. West Lava Camp; Three Creek L., border of meadow.

VIBURNUM L.

Viburnum pauciflorum Pylaie, T. & G. Fl. NA. 2:17. 1841. HIGH-BUSH CRANBERRY. Deciduous shrub, 1-2 m high; branches glabrous; leaves 4-9 cm long,

broadly oval, 3-lobed above the middle, broad at base, glabrous to loosely pubescent beneath, the petiole shorter than the blade; cymes small, on short twigs having a pair of leaves; flowers small, perfect, 5-lobed, white; stamens 5; fruit a drupe, 8-12 mm long, nearly globose, light red.

Rare in open woods along streams. C. Trout Cr. Swamp.

57. VALERIANACEAE   Valerian Family

Annual or perennial herbs; leaves opposite; perfect or unisexual; gamopetalous.

VALERIANA L.

Valeriana sitchensis Bong. Mem. Acad. St. Petersb. VI. 2:145. 1832. NORTHERN VALERIAN. Perennial herb, 30-60 cm high; rhizome stout, roots fibrous; leaves 3-5 foliate, the terminal leaflet much enlarged, leaf margins dentate; stamens 3, exserted, longer than the corolla-lobes; corolla white or pinkish, the tube gibbous; fruit a nutlet, oblong-ovate, 3-6 mm long.

Frequent in moist woods. H. Sand Spring; McKenzie Pass; Lake Valley; Obsidian Cliffs 1890 m (6200 ft); Sparks L.; Three Cr., meadow 1920 m (6300 ft).

58. COMPOSITAE   Sunflower Family

Herbs or shrubs, leaves without stipules, flowers borne in a close head on a common receptacle appearing as a single flower and surrounded by an involucre of bracts. Corollas are tubular or ligulate (strap-shaped).

Discoid head, bearing tubular flowers only.

Ligulate head, bearing strap-shaped flowers only.

Radiate head, when the outer corollas are ligulate and the inner tubular.

Receptacle may have scales or bracts (chaff) each subtending a flower. Calyx gamosepalys, the tube adherent to the ovary, the limb developed into various forms called the pappus which may be of capillary bristles, scales, awns, a ring (or crown), or wanting. Stamens 5 borne on the petals, the anthers usually united to form a tube around the 2-cleft style. Ovary inferior, 1-celled; fruit an achene.

KEY TO THE GENERA OF COMPOSITAE

Corollas all ligulate, 5-toothed; flowers perfect; milky juice

     Pappus of slender plumose bristles, achenes not bearded .... *Stephanomeria*

Pappus of capillary bristles, awns or paleae

     Pappus capillary, not broadened at base

Heads solitary on scape, leaves all basal ....*Agoseris*

Heads not solitary on each stem, leaves not all basal ....*Hieracium*

Pappus of narrow scales with long awns ....*Microseris*

Corollas all tubular, or ligulate and 3-toothed only in the marginal
        ones; ligulate flowers pistillate or neutral; watery juice
  Style branches club-shaped (clavate), little flattened; flowers tubular,
      perfect; corollas never yellow; bracts of the
      involucre 3-nerved or more; flowers purplish ....*Eupatorium*

  Style branches not clavate, bracts 1-nerved or nerveless
    Style branches tipped with a flat appendage; leaves alternate;
      ligules present or wanting; pappus of capillary
      bristles; receptacle naked
      Rays yellow
      Heads small, many ....*Solidago*

      Heads larger, solitary or few ....*Haplopappus*

      Rays blue, purple or white
      Involucral bracts in 1 or 2 series, linear or lance-linear;
        ray flowers usually narrower and more numerous ....*Erigeron*

      Involucral bracts in several series, broadly linear;
        ray flowers broader, fewer ....*Aster*

    Style branches not tipped with a flat appendage
    Receptacle densely long-bristly; ligules none ....*Cirsium*

    Receptacle without long dense bristles
      Bracts of the involucre scarious or wanting
        Pappus of capillary bristles; ligules none; plant white-woolly
        Pappus of pistillate flowers distinct;
          basal leaves soon withering ....*Anaphalis*

        Pappus of pistillate flowers united at base and falling
          together; basal leaves persisting ....*Antennaria*

        Pappus wanting; receptacle chaffy;
          involucral bracts appressed ....*Achillea*

      Bracts of the involucre mostly not scarious;
        little or not at all imbricated
      Pappus of soft capillary bristles
      Heads solitary on scape-like peduncles;
        plants low, woolly ....*Raillardella*

      Heads not solitary on scape-like peduncles;
        not low or woolly; heads radiate
      Leaves alternate; heads rather small;
        involucre with a few very small outer bracts ....*Senecio*

      Leaves opposite; heads large;
        involucre without small outer bracts ....*Arnica*

    Pappus of 4 lacerate paleae; leaves basal ....*Hulsea*

ACHILLEA L.

Achillea millefolium L. var. **lanulosa** (Nutt.) Piper, in Piper & Beattie, Fl. Palouse Reg. 196. 1901. YARROW. Perennial herb with strong scent, about 50 cm high; leaves alternate, pinnately-dissected, densely pubescent; corymbs of many radiate heads; margins of involucral bracts pale to brown; flowers white; ray-florets pistillate, disk-florets perfect; pappus none.

Frequent in dry open fields. H to T. McKenzie Pass; Lake Valley; Devils L.; Sparks L.; Broken Top above 2440 m (8000 ft).

A *Achillea millefolium lanulosa;* **B** *Agoseris aurantiaca;* **C** *Anaphalis margaritacea;*
D *Antennaria rosea;* **E** *Arnica mollis*

AGOSERIS Raf.

Agoseris aurantiaca (Hook.) Greene, Pittonia 2:177. 1891. ORANGE-FLOWERED AGOSERIS. Perennial herb with milky juice, 15-40 cm high; scapes slender, floccose-hairy, usually longer than the leaves; leaves all basal, variable, usually narrowly-linear; heads ligulate, solitary on the long scapes; corollas orange-bronze; beak of achene longer than the body; pappus about twice as long as the achene, capillary bristles white.

Occasional in moist sandy soil. H. Linton Cr. springs 1830 m (6000 ft); Mesa Cr.; Todd L.; Scott Mt.; Black Crater.

ANAPHALIS DC.

Anaphalis margaritacea (L.) Benth. & Hook., Gen. Pl. 2:303. 1873. PEARLY EVERLASTING. Perennial herb, white-woolly, 30-60 cm high; leaves alternate, sessile, entire, linear-lanceolate, dark-green, glabrate above, woolly beneath; heads numerous in small rounded panicles, mostly dioecious, discoid, many-flowered; corollas yellowish, filiform; involucral bracts pearly-white, scarious.

Occasional in open woods, H to T. Pine Butte; Lava Camp L.; Rock Mesa 2045 m (6700 ft).

Anaphalis margaritaceae L. var. **subalpina** Gray, Syn. Fl. 12:233. 1884. Differs from the species in being lower, with leaves woolly on both surfaces, inflorescence more compact.

Rare. H. Upper Soda Cr. 1740 m (5700 ft).

ANTENNARIA Gaertn.

Perennial, mat-forming white-woolly plants; leaves mostly entire, alternate, the basal more numerous, the cauline reduced upward; heads discoid; receptacle naked; flowers dioecious, the staminate with style entire, pappus a single row of bristles, clavate or barbellate; pistillate flowers with corollas narrowly-tubular, style bifid, pappus copious, bristles capillary, united at base and falling as a ring; achenes oblong, nearly terete.

KEY TO THE SPECIES OF ANTENNARIA

Upper scarious part of involucral bracts brownish or blackish-green
    Bracts blackish-green, usually sharp-pointed, mostly alpine plants ....*A. alpina var.*

    Bracts pale brown or becoming white at the tip, usually blunt;
    C to H Zone ....*A. umbrinella*

Upper scarious part of involucral bracts white or pink;
    lowlands to H Zone ....*A. rosea*

Antennaria alpina L. var. **media** (Greene) Jeps. Man. Fl. Pl. Calif. 1070. 1925. ALPINE EVERLASTING. Low cespitose perennial; leaves narrow, gray-tomentose; heads several grouped in dense clusters; involucral bracts usually narrow, pointed.

Frequent on higher slopes. A and H. Middle Sister; Camp Riley; Wickiup Plain.

Antennaria rosea Greene, Pittonia 3:281. 1898. ROSY EVERLASTING. Perennial 7-30 cm or more high, densely tomentose; basal leaves oblanceolate; heads several in a subcapitate cyme; involucral bracts of the pistillate heads deep rose-pink to bright or dull white.

Frequent in dry open woods and meadows. H to AT. Scott Mt.; Millican Crater Tr. at 1830 m (6000 ft); Camp Agoseris; Lake Valley; Sparks L.

Antennaria umbrinella Rydb. Bull. Torrey Club 24:302. 1897. BROWN EVERLASTING. Dense mat-forming perennial, gray-tomentose; heads several in a subcapitate cyme; achenes mostly glabrous; bristles of staminate pappus dilated above.

Rare in area. H to AT. Middle Sister, below timberline.

ARNICA Gaertn.

Heads mostly radiate, large, few; ray-flowers few, pistillate, fertile, yellow; disk-flowers perfect, fertile, yellow; involucre herbaceous, campanulate, the bracts narrow, equal; receptacle nearly flat, naked.

KEY TO THE SPECIES OF ARNICA

Cauline leaves mostly 5 or more pairs, ovate to lanceolate,
    toothed, more or less pubescent ....*A. amplexicaulis*

Cauline leaves mostly 2-4 pairs (basal leaves not included)
   Pappus subplumose, tawny
      Heads broad, subhemispheric; cauline leaves variable in shape,
         mostly lanceolate or oblanceolate, entire or denticulate ....*A. mollis*

      Heads narrower; cauline leaves ovate, deltoid to
         broadly elliptic, irregularly toothed ....*A. diversifolia*

   Pappus barbellate, white or nearly so
      Achenes glabrous, at least below; basal leaves
         seldom cordate, more or less serrate ....*A. latifolia* var.

      Achenes short-pubescent nearly or quite to the base;
         lower leaves strongly cordate, serrate or entire ....*A. cordifolia*

Arnica amplexicaulis Nutt., Trans. Am. Phil. Soc. 7:408. 1841. CLASPING ARNICA. Perennial herb, 30 cm or more high, sparsely villous; leaves opposite mostly clasping; pappus tawny, subplumose; achenes sparsely hairy.

Infrequent in open woods. H. Spring L.; Middle Sister 2250 m (7400 ft).

Arnica cordifolia Hook. Fl. Bor. Am. 1:331. 1840. HEART-LEAVED ARNICA. Perennial herb, 15-30 cm high, thinly glandular-pubescent; leaves cordate, usually toothed; pappus barbellate, white; achenes pubescent, sometimes glandular.

Rare in dry open woods. H to AT. Black Crater 2180 m (7150 ft).

Arnica diversifolia Greene, Pittonia 4:171. 1900. STICKY ARNICA. Perennial herb, 15-30 cm high, glandular-puberulent; leaves ovate or deltoid, irregularly toothed; disk flowers few; ray flowers about 10-12; pappus subplumose, light tawny; achenes short-hairy.

Rare. Rocky slopes. A. Little Brother 2290 m (7500 ft).

Arnica latifolia Bong. var. **gracilis** (Rydb.)

Cronq. in Hitchcock et al Vas. Pl. Pac. NW 5:51. 1955. MOUNTAIN ARNICA. Perennial herb, 15-30 cm high, tufted; stems several from the rhizone; cauline leaves 2-4 pairs, broadly lanceolate; heads 1-several, small; achenes glabrous, glandular or hairy.

Rare on higher slopes. H and A. Camp Agoseris 1890 m (6200 ft).

Arnica mollis., Fl. Bor. Am. 1:331. 1840. SOFT-LEAVED ARNICA. Perennial herb, 25-60 cm high, glandular-pubescent; cauline leaves 3-4 pairs, sessile, ovate, lanceolate, obovate to oblanceolate; heads 1-few, broad.

Frequent in moist meadows and woods. H. Pole Bridge; Frog Camp; Middle and South Sister; Linton Meadows; Skyline Tr. at Mesa Cr. 1770 m (5800 ft); Soda Cr.; Green Lakes.

ASTER L.

Perennial herbs; leaves alternate, simple; heads radiate, solitary or many; rays not numerous, shades of purple, blue, white; pappus copius, of capillary bristles; achenes 4-5-nerved.

KEY TO THE SPECIES OF ASTER

Plants with a caudex and woody taproot
   Stems simple, scapose; heads solitary, large; leaves
      narrow, long, entire, glabrous, chiefly basal ....*A. alpigenus*

   Stems branching; heads several, small; leaves small,
      broad, mostly entire, canescent ....*A. shastensis* var.

Plants with a rhizome and fibrous roots
   Rays few, 8 or less; leaves more or less densely tomentose beneath,
      the lower reduced, the others numerous, narrowly elliptic ....*A. ledophyllus*

   Rays more numerous; lower cauline leaves not clearly reduced,
      not densely tomentose beneath

      Leaves broadly lanceolate, strongly toothed, not clasping at base ....*A. radulinus*
      Leaves narrower, to linear, entire clasping at base
         Leaves narrowly-lanceolate, at least 8 times as long as wide;

involucral bracts white-margined ....*A. occidentalis*
Leaves oblanceolate, 5-15 cm long, mostly glabrous;

   involucral bracts mostly green ....*A. foliaceus* var.

Aster alpigenus (T. & G.) Gray, Proc. Am. Acad. 8:389. ALPINE ASTER. Perennial, 5-25 cm high; thick branching caudex with long fleshy taproot; heads solitary borne on ascending scapes above the basal leaves; leaves as much as 15 cm long, linear-oblanceolate, entire, glabrous; cauline leaves few, much reduced; rays lavender; achene glabrous except at apex.

Common in alpine meadows. A and H. Lake Valley; Obsidian Cliffs; Middle Sister above Sunshine Shelter 2290 m (7500 ft); Mesa Cr.; Goose Cr.; South Sister.

Aster foliaceus Lindl. var. **parryi** (D. C. Eaton) Gray. Syn. Fl. 1²:193. 1884. LEAFY ASTER. Perennial, 20-45 cm high; fibrous rooted, woody base; leaves lanceolate or oblanceolate; rays light purple; achenes pubescent.

Common in NW section of area in meadows and open woods. H. Lake Valley; Frog Camp; White Branch Cr. at 1800 m (5900 ft).

Aster ledophyllus Gray, Proc. Am. Acad. 16:98. 1880. CASCADE ASTER. Perennial, 30-60 cm high; woody base; lower leaves small and scale-like, the others many, alike, elliptic, mostly entire, mostly glabrous above, lighter and tomentose below, often densely so; rays light purple; achenes pubescent.

Common in open woods. H. Pine Butte; Windy Point; Lake Valley; White Branch Cr.; Tenas Lakes; Green Lakes area.

Aster occidentalis (Nutt.) T. & G. Fl. N. Am. 2:164. 1841. WESTERN MOUNTAIN ASTER. Perennial, 30-45 cm high, solitary or few in a cluster; leaves narrowly-elliptic, entire or remotely serrate, glabrous; rays violet; achenes pubescent.

Frequent in open woods. H and C. Scott L.; Fall Cr.; Obsidian Cliffs.

Aster radulinus Gray, Proc. Am. Acad. 8:388. 1872. ROUGH-LEAVED ASTER. Perennial, 15 cm or more high; woody rhizome; stems short-pubescent; leaves broadly oblanceolate to ovate, serrate, glabrate

above, harsh-pubescent below; rays purple; achenes hairy.

Rare in area. Lower H to T. McKenzie Pass, Sand Hills.

Aster shastensis Gray var. **latifolius** Cronq. in Hitchcock et al Vasc. Pl. Pac. NW. 5:94. 1955. SHASTA ASTER. Perennial, 5-10 cm high; slender branching caudex, with taproot; plant grayish with incurved hairs; leaves small, entire or toothed, spatulate, petiolate; heads few to many; involucral bracts purple-red; rays purple; achenes pubescent.

Rare in dry sandy soil. H. Rock Mesa; South Sister 2135-2440 m (7000-8000 ft).

CIRSIUM Mill.

Biennial or perennial herbs, stout, spiny; leaves alternate, variously toothed, spine-tipped; heads rather large, discoid, usually in small clusters; pappus of plumose bristles united at base.

Cirsium centaureae (Rydb.) K. Schum. Just. Bot. Jahresb. 29¹:566. 1903. FRINGED-BRACT THISTLE. Perennial herb, with taproot; stems 45-60 cm high, slender, thinly floccose; leaves narrow, oblong, deeply lobed, the lobes spine-tipped, green and glabrate or thinly-tomentose above, lighter and thinly-floccose-tomentose beneath; heads 1-3 mostly at the ends of branches; involucre 1.5-2.5 cm high, the bracts glabrous or thinly arachnoid, laciniate-fringed, scarious; corollas light purple.

Frequent in dry open woods and sandy places. H. Pine Butte; Pole Bridge; Scott Mt.; summit; Wickiup Plain; Soda Spg.

ERIGERON L.

Annual or perennial herbs; leaves alternate, entire or dissected; heads solitary or few, radiate usually or discoid; involucral bracts narrow, receptacle flat or slightly convex, naked; pappus of capillary bristles, with or without a row of minute outer scales or bristles.

KEY TO THE SPECIES OF ERIGERON

Leaves palmately 3-4-dissected ....*E. compositus* var.
Leaves mostly entire
   Heads small, rays short and very narrow ....*E. acris* var. *debilis*
   Heads larger, rays longer, up to 1.3 cm, and 0.3 cm wide ....*E. peregrinus* ssp.

A *Erigeron peregrinus callianthemus;* **B** *Erigeron acris debilis;* **C** *Aster alpigenus;*
D *Aster ledophyllus*

Erigeron acris L. var. **debilis** Gray, Syn. Fl. 1²:220. 1884. BITTER ERIGERON. Perennial about 15 cm high; leaves oblanceolate, entire, the cauline reduced upward; heads small; rays numerous, light purple, very narrow; pappus pale brown, capillary.

Rare in open rocky ground. Lower H. Hand L. 1465 m (4800 ft).

Erigeron compositus Pursh var. **glabratus** Macoun, Cat. Can. Pl. 2:231. 1884. CUT-LEAF FLEABANE. Perennial, 8 cm or less high; branching caudex and long taproot; leaves 3-ternate, the divisions not linear; herbage quite hairy and glandular; rays light purple, pink or white.

Infrequent on dry rocky slopes. A and upper H. Little Brother 2380 m (7800 ft); above Sunshine Shelter; Broken Top, about 2440 m (8000 ft).

Erigeron peregrinus Greene ssp. **callianthemus** (Greene) Conq. in Hitchcock et al Vas. Pl. Pac. NW. 5:188. 1955. ASTER ERIGERON. Perennial, about 30 cm high; stout rhizome with fibrous roots; leaves spatulate, entire, ciliate, the upper clasping; heads large, solitary; rays purplish-blue, about 3 mm wide; achenes pubescent.

Frequent in moist meadows and open places. H. Pine Butte; Sunshine Shelter; Linton Meadows; Wickiup Plain; Sparks L.; Green Lakes 2000 m (6550 ft).

EUPATORIUM L.

Eupatorium occidentale Hook. Fl. Bor. Am. 1:305. 1833. WESTERN EUPATORIUM. Erect perennial, 30-45 cm high; clustered stems mostly simple; leaves alternate, or a few opposite below, numerous, ovate with truncate base, dentate, gland-dotted beneath, short petioled; heads discoid, small, clustered; flowers perfect, purple-pink; pappus of barbellate bristles, dingy-white; achenes 5-angled, glandular-dotted, about 4 mm long.

Rare. Dry rocky places. Lower H and C. Benson L. 1615 m (5300 ft).

HAPLOPAPPUS Cass.

Haplopappus bloomeri Gray, Proc. Am. Acad. 6:540. 1865. RABBIT BRUSH. Broad compact shrub, 15-50 cm high, thinly tomentose, glandular-dotted or puberulent; leaves numerous, linear to narrowly oblanceolate, about 2.5 cm long; heads numerous, one or several to a branch, few-flowered; 3-4 ray-florets, yellow; 5-10 disk-florets; pappus tawny, slightly barbellate; achenes pubescent.

Occasional in sandy soil. H to AT. Windy Point; South Matthieu L. 1860 m (6100 ft); Pole Bridge; White Branch Cr.; Obsidian Cliffs.

HIERACIUM L.

Perennial herbs, fibrous-rooted, milky juice; leaves alternate or all basal, entire or toothed; flowers all ligulate, perfect; receptacle naked; achenes not beaked; pappus whitish to light brown.

A *Haplopappus bloomeri*; **B** *Hulsea nana*; **C** *Hieracium gracile*

KEY TO THE SPECIES OF HIERACIUM

Flowers white, stellate-pubescence lacking ....*H. albiflorum*

Flowers yellow, stellate-pubescence present
Plants 30-50 cm high, leaves long-setose, entire, lanceolate ....*H. cynoglossoides*

Plants 15-30 cm high, leaves entire, or densely long-setose
Leaves glabrous, all basal ....*H. gracile*

Leaves densely long-setose, not all basal ....*H. horridum*

Hieracium albiflorum Hook. Fl. Bor. Am. 1:298. 1833. WHITE-FLOWERED HAWKWEED. Stems few, 30-50 cm high from a woody caudex; glabrous above, loosely long-villous below; leaves reduced upward, the lower clustered at the base, oblanceolate, mostly entire, sparsely long-hairy to quite densely so; heads several, flowers white; pappus white or dingy, longer than the achene.

Occasional in open woods. H to T. Pine Butte; Lake Valley; White Branch Cr.; Sparks L.

Hieracium cynoglossoides Arvet-Touv. Spicil. Hier. 20. 1881. HOUNDS-TONGUE HAWKWEED. Plant rather slender; involucre densely stellate-pubescent with many longer, black, gland-tipped hairs; stem stellate, the lower with added bristles; leaves lanceolate to oblanceolate, mostly entire. 7.5-10 cm long, covered with stellate hairs interspersed with stiff bristly hairs; inflorescence several-flowered; ligules yellow, pappus sordid.

Rare. Observed only in yellow-pine forest, eastern slope. AT. Road to Trout Cr. Swamp.

Hieracium gracile Hook., Fl. Bor. Am. 1:298. 1833. ALPINE HAWKWEED. Slender perennial, stellate-pubescent; leaves all basal, mostly glabrous, spatulate, tapering to long petiole; involucral bracts with black setae, gland-tipped; flowers yellow; pappus dingy.

Frequent in open woods to timberline. H. Pine Butte; Scott Mt.; White Branch Cr. at trail crossing; Middle Sister at 2320 m (7600 ft); Mesa Creek; Wickiup Plain; Green Lakes.

Hieracium horridum Fries. Epic. Hier. 154. 1862. SHAGGY HAWKWEED. Stems few, clustered; leaves spatulate, narrowing to base; entire plant covered with dense, long, shaggy, light brown hairs; heads small; flowers yellow; pappus brown.

Rare, in woods. H. Mesa Cr. at 1770 m (5800 ft).

HULSEA T. & G.

Hulsea nana Gray, Pac. R. Rep. 6:76. 1855. DWARF HULSEA. Perennial herb, cespitose, mostly 5-10 cm high, densely glandular-villous; long stout taproot; branching caudex; leaves mainly basal, pinnately shallowly-lobed; heads large, solitary on the naked flowering stems; corollas yellow; pappus of 4 lacerate scales.

Frequent above timberline to highest peaks in loose rocks. A. Black Crater; North, South and Middle Sister; Broken Top; Ball Butte 2470 m (8100 ft).

MICROSERIS D. Don

Microseris alpestris (Gray) Q. Jones in Hitchcock et al Vas. Pl. Pac. NW. 5:267. 1955. ALPINE MICROSERIS. (*Agoseris alpestris* Greene, Pittonia 2:177. 1891). Perennial herb, 10-25 cm high, scapose, glabrous, milky juice; fleshy taproot; leaves basal, 7:5-15 cm long, narrow; variable, from entire to remotely toothed or deeply pinnated cut into many narrow segments. Heads solitary, 10-flowered or more, the corollas yellow-orange; pappus of white, distinctly barbellate bristles; achenes narrowed at top, not beaked.

Frequent in woods and meadows at higher elevations. H. McKenzie Pass; Black Crater; Frog Camp; Camp Agoseris (Camp Riley); Sunshine Shelter; Ball Butte at 2180 m (7150 ft); Three Creek L.

RAILLARDELLA Benth. & Hook.

Raillardella argentea Gray, Bot. Calif. 1:417. 1876. SILVERY RAILLARDELLA. Perennial, scapes 7.5-10 cm high, stipitate-glandular; branching caudex and creeping rhizomes forming dense mats; leaves narrow, oblanceolate with copious silky, silvery hairs; heads solitary, discoid; florets yellow; involucre glandular; pappus white, strongly plumose; achenes narrow, pubescent.

Occasional in open woods and sandy slopes. H and A. Middle and South Sister; Mesa Cr.; Green Lakes.

SENECIO L.

Perennial herbs, leaves alternate, heads radiate, the rays yellow, receptacle flat, not chaffy, pappus of soft white bristles.

A *Microseris alpestris*; **B** *Senecio triangularis*; **C** *Solidago canadensis elongata*;
D *Raillardella argentea*

KEY TO THE SPECIES OF SENECIO

Stem leaves well developed, not tufted at base
  Low plants, stems decumbent, leaves glabrous,
    somewhat fleshy, obovate, toothed ....*S. fremontii*

  Taller plants; stems erect; leaves nearly glabrous, gradually
    reduced upward, broadly to narrowly triangular with arrow- or
    heart-shaped base, sharply dentate, the lower long-petiolate ....*S. triangularis*

Stem leaves few, reduced or none, basal leaves subround, obovate,
  spatulate, crenate-dentate to deeply lobed ....*S. subnudus*

Senecio fremontii T. & G. Fl. 2:445. 1843. LOW MOUNTAIN SENECIO. Perennial, about 15 cm high, glabrous, branching caudex, taproot; leaves thick, about 2 cm long; heads terminal, few; rays 6-8 mm long.

Occasional above timberline in rocky volcanic soil. A. Little Brother 2380 m (7800 ft); Sunshine Shelter; South Sister; Broken Top.

Senecio subnudus DC. Prod. 6:428. 1837. FEW-LEAVED SENECIO. Perennial, 7.5-15 cm high; heads 1 or 2 on slender simple stems, glabrous; rays 7-8 mm long.

Frequent in wet meadows. II. Lake Valley; South Sister; Green Lakes; Three Creek L. area.

Senecio triangularis Hook. Fl. Bor. Am. 1:332. 1833. SPEAR-HEAD SENECIO. Stems one to several, glabrate, 50-100 cm or more high; heads several in a short flat-topped inflorescence; rays about 8, 8-10 mm long.

Common in damp woods and meadows. Lower H to C. Lake Valley; Scott Mt.; Sunshine Shelter; Sparks L.; Black Crater.

SOLIDAGO L.

Perennial herbs; leaves alternate, simple, usually narrow; heads radiate, small; rays short, yellow; receptacle naked; ascenes pubescent, few-ribbed; pappus a single row of capillary bristles.

KEY TO THE SPECIES OF SOLIDAGO

Low alpine plants, glabrous; leaves broad ....*S. spathulata* var. *nana*

Taller plants, stems pubescent, leaves elliptic,
  4 times longer than broad ....*S. canadensis* var. *elongata*

Solidago canadensis L. var. **elongata** (Nutt.) M. E. Peck, Man. High. Pl. Ore. 774. 1961. NARROW GOLDENROD. Stems 30-60 cm high, from creeping rhizomes; inflorescence compact; heads numerous, small; achenes with fine stiff hairs.

Frequent in open woods and meadows. Lower H to C. Lake Valley; Frog Camp; Benson L.

Solidago spathulata DC var. **nana,** Cronquist in Hitchcock et al. Vas. Pl. Pac. NW. 5:311. 1955. DWARF GOLDENROD. Stems 7.5-15 cm high; leaves obovate or spatulate, dentate; heads relatively few.

Infrequent above timebrline. A. South Sister 2440 m (8000 ft).

STEPHANOMERIA Nutt.

Stephanomeria lactucina Gray, Proc. Amer. Acad. 6:551. 1865. LARGE FLOWERED STEPHANOMERIA. Slender somewhat branching perennial, about 15 cm high, milky juice, glabrous; leaves alternate, about 5 cm long, linear entire or with a few straight retrorsely curved teeth; heads few, rather large; flowers pink; pappus entirely plumose.

Rare east of divide in dry woods. AT. Trout Cr. Swamp road 1165 m (3800 ft).

REFERENCES CITED

Abrams, LeRoy, 1923-44-51-60, An illustrated flora of the Pacific states: Vols. I-IV. Stanford Univ. Press

Applegate, Elmer I., 1939, Plants of the Crater Lake National Park: Am. Midl. Nat. Vol. 22, No. 2

Bailey, Vernon, 1936, The Mammals and life zones of Oregon: U.S. Dept. Agr. N. Am. Fauna No. 55

Baker, Wm. H., 1951, Plants of Fairview Mt. Calapooya Range, Oregon: Am. Midl. Nat. Vol. 46, No. 1

Benson, Gilbert T., 1930, The Trees and Shrubs of western Oregon: Stanford Univ. Press

Benson, Lyman, 1949, A Treatise on the North American Ranunculi: Am. Midl. Nat. Vol. 40, No. 1

Daubenmire, R. F., 1943, Vegetational zonation in the Rocky Mountains: Bot. Rev. Vol. 9, No. 6

Gilkey, Helen M., 1936, Handbook of Northwest flowering plants: Metropolitan Press

Hitchcock, A. S., 1950, Manual of the grasses of the United States. 2nd edition revised by Agnes Chase. U.S. Dept. Agr. Misc. Publ. No. 200

Hitchcock, C. Leo, Arthur Cronquist, Marion Ownbey and **J. W. Thompson,** 1955-64, Vascular plants of the Pacific Northwest: Part 2, 3, 4, 5. Univ. Wash. Press

Hodge, Edwin T., 1925, Mount Multnomah, ancient ancestor of the Three Sisters: Univ. Oregon

Howell, Thomas, 1897, A Flora of Northwest America

Jepson, Willis L., 1925, A Manual of the flowering plants of California: Assoc. Students Store, Univ. Calif.

Jones, George N., 1938, The Flowering plants and ferns of Mt. Rainier: Univ. Wash.

Keck, David D., 1945, Studies in Penstemon VIII: Am. Midl. Nat. Vol. 33, No. 1

Merriam, C. H., 1894, The Geographic distribution of animals and plants in North America: U.S. Dept. Agr. Yearbook, Govt. Printing Office, Washington

Newberry, John S., 1857, Pacific Railroad Surveys, Vol. 6. War Dept. U.S.A.

Peck, Morton E., 1961, A Manual of the higher plants of Oregon: 2nd edition. Binfords & Mort

Piper, Charles V., 1906, Flora of the State of Washington: Contr. U.S. Natl. Herb. Vol. XI

Piper, Charles V. and **R. Kent Beattie,** 1915, Flora of the Norhwest Coast:

Rydberg, Per Axel, 1917, Flora of the Rocky Mountains and adjacent plains: N.Y. Bot. Gard.

St. John, Harold and **Edith Hardin,** 1929, Flora of Mount Baker: Mazama, Vol. 11, No. 12

Sudworth, George B., 1908, Forest trees of the Pacific slope: Forest Service, U.S. Dept. Agr.

Tidestrom, Ivar, 1925, Flora of Utah and Nevada: Contr. U.S. Natl. Herb. Vol. 25

U.S. Dept. Agriculture, 1941, Climate and man: in Yearbook of Agriculture. Govt. Printing Office, Washington

Williams, Howel, 1944, Volcanoes of the Three Sisters region. Oregon Cascades: Univ. Calif. Press

Wynd, F. Lyle, 1936, A Flora of Crater Lake National Park: Am. Midl. Nat. Vol. 17, No. 6

GLOSSARY

A—: A prefix meaning not. Without apetalous, not having petals.

Acaulescent: Without a true leafy stem, the leaves in a tuft at the base, the flowers borne on a scape or stalk. e.g. Dandelion.

Acerose: With a sharp slender needle-like point.

Achene (akene): A dry indehiscent 1-celled fruit.

Acuminate: Tapering gradually at the apex or end.

Acute: Ending with a sharp point. .

Adnate: United with another body or part of a different series.

Alternate: Leaves, one from each node; not opposite.

Ament: A catkin; a bracted pendulous spike. Willows, alders.

Amplexicaul: Said of a leaf with a base clasping the stem.

Androgynous: Having both staminate and pistillate flowers in the same spike, the latter being below the staminate. The converse of gynaecandrous.

Annual: A plant completing the life-cycle in one year.

Anterior: The side in front; in an axillary flower the side away from the stem.

Anther: The pollen-bearing part of the stamen.

Anthesis: The time of flowering, anthers shedding pollen, the stigma receptive.

Apiculate: Ending in a short sharp abrupt rather soft tip, as of leaves.

Appressed: Flattened or pressed closely against another part or organ, as of leaves against the stem.

Approximate: Situated close together but not united.

Aquatic: Growing in water.

Arachnoid: Having cobwebby hairs.

Arcuate: Curved or bent like a bow.

Aril: An appendage or covering of certain seeds developing as an outgrowth from the summit of the seed stalk.

Arillate: Furnished with an aril.

Aristate: Having an awn or bristle, as with many grasses.

Articulate: Jointed.

Ascending: Growing obliquely upward.

Attenuate: With a very slender narrow prolongation.

Auricled: With small ear-like appendages, as at the base of the petiole.

Awn: A bristle-like appendage, as on the floral parts of grasses.

Awned: Provided with an awn or bristle.

Axil: The angle above the attachment of a leaf or branch to the stem.

Axillary: Occuring or borne at an axil.

Axis: The stem or central support on which parts or organs are arranged.

Banner or **standard:** The upper petal in a papilionaceous or pea flower.

Barb: A bristle having one or more sharp rigid reflexed points.

Barbate: Bearded, the hairs long and stiff.

Barbed: Beset with barbs.

Barbellate: Minutely bearded with short stiff hairs; sometimes used to indicate "barbed."

Beak: A narrow elongated appendage near the tip of a structure.

Berry: A fleshy indehiscent fruit formed from a single ovary.

Bi—: A prefix meaning two or twice.

Bidentate: Having two tooth-like prolongations.

Biennial: A plant requiring two growing seasons to complete the life-cycle.

Bilabiate: Two-lipped, calyx or corolla.

Bilobate: Two-lobed.

Bipinnate: Twice pinnate.

Bipinnatifid: Pinnatifid with the primary segments again pinnatifid.

Blade: The flat expanded portion of a leaf or petal.

Bloom: The fine powdery deposit on a fruit. See glaucous.

Bract: A modified leaf, usually small, subtending a flower or cluster of flowers.

Bracteate: With bracts.

Bractlet: A small or secondary bract.

Bulb: An underground modified leaf-bud composed of fleshy storage scales.

Bulblet: A small bulb-like fleshy bud often borne on the stem.

Caducous: Falling very early, as the caducous sepals of poppies.

Callus: Hardened tissue or point; the tough often hairy swelling at the base of the lemma and palea in grasses.

Calyculate: Having short bracts at the outer base of the involucre proper in some Compositae.

Calyx: The outer set of the perianth or floral envelope; the sepals as a unit.

Campanulate: Bell-shaped.

Canaliculate: Channeled longitudinally.

Canescent: Grayish white or hoary due to fine dense pubescence.

Capillary: Hair-like.

Capitate: Borne in a dense head-like cluster.

Capsule: A pod; a dry dehiscent fruit or seed-vessel composed of two or more carpels.

Carinate: Having a keel or sharp ridge.

Carpel: A single pistil or one of the elements of a compound pistil.

Caryopsis: A grain; the fruit of a grass, the seed and fruit united.

Catkin: An ament; a bracted pendulous spike.

Caudate: Having a tail-like appendage.

Caudex: The short stout persistent often woody base of a perennial herb.

Caulescent: Having a distinct leafy stem above ground. The opposite of acaulescent.

Cauline: Pertaining to or borne on a stem, as cauline leaves.

Cell: A chamber or compartment in which seeds or pollen grains are borne; the structural unit of an organism.

Cespitose: Tufted; producing many closely clustered stems from a single branched base.

Chaff: Thin dry scales or bracts in some flower clusters.

Chartaceous: Paper-like in texture.

Chlorophyll: The green colored complex substance occuring in most plants and essential for the production of food elements necessary for maintaining their existence.

Ciliate: Having the margin bordered with a row of hairs (cilia).

Cinerous: Of ashen hue.

Circinate: Rolled into a coil from the tip.

Circumscissile: Splitting transversely, at right angles to the long axis.

Clavate: Club-shaped.

Claw: The narrow claw-like base of a petal.

Cleft: Cut about halfway to the midvein or base, as of leaves.

Coalescent: Parts of a kind united.

Coherent: United with another body or organ of the same kind.

Cohesion: The union of one organ with another of the same kind.

Coma: A tuft of hairs, as at one end of a seed; comose, furnished with a coma.

Commissure: The plane by which the flattened faces of the two carpels in Umbelliferae cohere.

Complete: Said of a flower which has all four circles: sepals, petals, stamens, pistils.

Compressed: Flattened laterally or on the sides.

Conduplicate: Folded lengthwise.

Cone: The dry multiple fruit of most Gymnosperms and somewhat similar structures of a few Angiosperms.

Confluent: Blended in one.

Coniferous: Cone-bearing.

Connate: United from the beginning.

Connective: The tissue between the two cells of an anther.

Connivent: Bending inward bringing the tips close together; lightly joined.

Contorted: Bent or twisted.

Convolute: Rolled inward from one side to the other.

Cordate: Heart-shaped; notched with two rounded lobes at the base.

Coriaceous: Leathery in texture.

Corm: A short thickened underground stem; solid and usually more or less globose.

Corolla: The inner set of the perianth or floral envelope; the petals as a unit.

Corymb: An open flower-cluster in which the outer and lower flowers bloom earliest and on the longest pedicels in such a way as to cause the inflorescence to be flat-topped.

Costate: Ribbed.

Creeping: Said of stems lying flat on the ground and rooting.

Crenate: Scolloped; having broad rounded teeth on the margin.

Crenulate: Minutely crenate.

Culm: The hollow or pithy stem of grasses and sedges.

Cuneate: Wedge-shaped; from a narrowed base gradually widening upward.

Cuspidate: Tipped with a sharp rigid point from a rounded apex.

Cyme: A flower-cluster in which the central or terminal flower blooms earliest. A cyme may be flat-topped.

Deciduous: Falling away, not persistent or evergreen. Separating after normal functioning is completed.

Decompound: More than once compound, leaves mostly.

Decumbent: Lying on the ground with the end ascending.

Decurrent: When the leaf-blade continues down the stem causing a winged appearance.

Decussate: Said of leaves arranged in pairs at right angles to the adjacent pair above or below.

Deflexed: Bent abruptly downward.

Dehiscent: Opening by valves, slits, etc. to discharge seeds or pollen.

Deltoid: Triangular, attached at the middle of the base.

Dentate: Toothed, the teeth standing directly outward.

Denticulate: Finely dentate.

Depauperate: Dwarfed. Said of plants small impoverished underdeveloped.

Depressed: (fruit) Flattened dorsoventrally or vertically. (stems) With branches spreading on the ground.

Dextrorse: Spirally twisting to the right. Said of vines that twine counterclockwise, as hops.

Di—: A prefix meaning two or twice. Same as bi—.

Diadelphous: Stamens united into two groups.

Dichotomous: Repeatedly forking into two equal branches.

Didymous: Twin, found in pairs.

Didynamous: Having four stamens arranged in two pairs, one pair longer than the other.

Diffuse: Numerous long loosely and widely spreading branches.

Digitate: Palmate. Leaflets all borne in the apex of the petiole.

Dilated: Widened or broadened. Dilatation, that which is dilated.

Dimorphic: Having two unlike forms.

Dioecious: (of two households) Plants one-sexed; stamens and pistils produced by different individual plants.

Discoid: In Compositae, heads bearing only flowers with tubular corollas.

Discrete: Separate, said of organs when they are neither crowded nor remote.

Disk: An enlargement of the receptacle at the base of the ovary.

Disk-flower: Tubular flower, in Compositae.

Dissected: Deeply cut or divided into numerous fine or narrow segments. Said mainly of leaves.

Distal: Away from the point of attachment. Opposed to proximal.

Distichous: Arranged to two ranks.

Distinct: Completely separate; not united.

Divaricate: Widely spreading; diverging at a wide angle.

Divided: (leaves) When the margin is indented to the midrib or base but the segments are not quite distinct.

Dorsal: Upon or relating to the back; outer or lower surface of an organ; posterior. Opposed to ventral.

Drupe: A fruit with a fleshy or pulpy outside and a hard stony inner portion enclosing the seed, as a cherry.

Elliptic: Having the shape of an ellipse, two or three times as long as broad, the sides with a uniform curvature.

Emarginate: Having a rather shallow notch at the apex.

Emersed: Growing up out of the water.

Endemic: Indigenous or native in a certain limited area or region.

Ensiform: Shaped like a dagger-blade.

Entire: With a smooth margin entirely without indentations.

Ephemeral: Lasting but a day; evanescent.

Epigynous: With the floral parts as if inserted on the summit of the ovary, the ovary being inferior.

Epipetalous: Borne on the petals or corolla.

Epiphyte: A plant growing upon another but not as a parasite.

Equilateral: Equal sided; same number of parts on a side.

Equitant: Basal leaves folded over each other, astride, flattened, as with *Iris*.

Erose: As of gnawed on the edge.

Excurrent: Running out. Said of a leaf or bract when the midrib projects beyond forming an awn-like appendage. The trunk of a tree is excurrent when it forms one main longitudinal axis, as in *Pinus*.

Exfoliating: Peeling off in layers.

Exserted: Projecting beyond any enveloping organs.

Exstipulate: Without stipules.

Extrorse: Turned outward.

Falcate: Sickle shaped.

Fascicle: A close cluster or bundle.

Fastigiate: With clustered parallel branches.

Fibrillose: When splitting into fibers.

Filament: A thread; the stalk bearing the anther.

Filiform: Thread-like.

Fimbriate: Fringed. Fimbrillate, minutely fringed.

Fistulous: Hollow.

Flaccid: Lax, drooping.

Flexuous: More or less zigzag or wavy.

Floccose: With loose tufts of wooly hairs.

Floret: A single simple very small flower of a cluster, especially of a grass.

Foliaceous: Leaf-like.

Follicle: A dry dehiscent pod developed from a simple pistil and opening along one suture only.

Forked: Dividing into two equal branches.

Free: Not attached to other organs.

Frond: The leaf of a fern.

Fruit: The mature ovary containing the seed, and often included are specially modified structures such as receptacle, bracts or calyx.

Funnelform: Gradually widening upward.

Fusiform: Spindle-shaped; thickest at the middle, tapering to each end.

Galea: The helmet-like upper lip of the corolla in the Mint and Figwort families. Galeate, having a galea.

Gamopetalous: The petals more or less united.

Gamosepalous: The sepals more or less united.

Geminate: In twos; twin.

Geniculate: Knee-like; sharply bent.

Gibbous: Swollen on one side.

Glabrate: Becoming glabrous or nearly so.

Glabrous: Without hairs.

Glandular: Having glands. Some hairs bear a gland at the tip.

Glaucous: Covered with a whitish bloom of fine waxen powder.

Globose: Globe-shaped; spherical.

Glochidiate: (bristles) Barb-tipped; apex with twin small sharp reflexed barbs.

Glomerate: Compacted into a close cluster.

Glomerule: A compacted head-like cyme.

Glume: One of the two empty lowest bracts on the spikelet in grasses.

Glutinous: Covered with a sticky exudation.

Gynaecandrous: (*Carex*) with pistillate and staminate flowers in the same spikelet, the pistillate above. The converse of androgynous.

Gynobase: An elevation of the receptacle in the Boraginaceae, bearing the carpels or nutlets.

Hastate: Spear-shaped, the basal lobes turned outward.

Head: A globose cluster of flowers sessile on the summit of the peduncle.

Herb: A plant without perennial woody parts above ground.

Herbaceous: Like an herb; free of woody tissue.

Herbage: The vegetative parts mainly stems and leaves.

Hirsute: With coarse straight beard-like hairs.

Hispid: With stiff bristle-like hairs.

Hyaline: Thin, translucent.

Hypogynous: Inserted on the receptacle below and free from the ovary; the ovary superior.

Imbricate: Overlapping like the shingles on a roof.

Immersed: Growing under water.

Imperfect: Flowers unisexual; lacking stamens or pistil.

Impressed: Below the general surface.

Incised: (leaves) The margins sharply and irregularly cut.

Included: Not extending beyond the surrounding organ.

Incomplete: (flowers) Lacking any of the four circles.

Indefinite: Numerous; variable in number.

Indehiscent: Not splitting open spontaneously at maturity.

Indigenous: Native to a region.

Indurated: Hardened.

Indusium: In ferns the scale-like membrane covering the sporangia.

Inferior: (ovary) Below the other organs; having the calyx corolla and stamens borne above or on the summit.

Inflated: Distended, bladder-like.

Inflorescence: The flowering part of a plant and its arrangement.

Inserted: Growing upon.

Internode: The portion of the stem between the nodes.

Interrupted: Not continuous and uniform.

Introduced: Brought in from some other region; not native.

Introrse: Facing inward.

Involucel: A secondary involucre as that of an umbellet.

Involucre: One or more whorls of bracts subtending a flower or flower cluster.

Involute: Both margins rolled inward.

Irregular: Parts not of the same size and shape.

Keel: A longitudinal ridge on the back of an organ.

Labiate: Having the calyx or corolla lipped.

Lacerate: Margins irregularly cut or torn.

Laciniate: Margins cut into deep narrow lobes.

Lanate: Woolly; covered with dense soft long hairs.

Lanceolate: Lance-shaped; several times longer than broad and tapering from below the middle to the narrowed base and the acute apex.

Latex: The milky juice of some plants.

Lax: Loose.

Leaflet: One of the divisions of a compound leaf.

Legume: A dry dehiscent one-celled fruit splitting front and back; a plant of the Leguminosae (Pea Family).

Lemma: The lowest bract enclosing the floret in grasses.

Lenticular: Shaped like a double-convex lens.

Ligneous: Woody.

Ligulate: Having a ligule.

Ligule: The short strap-shaped corolla of the ray flower in Compositae; in grasses it is the exserted part of the hyaline membrane lining the sheath at the base of the leaf.

Limb: A border or edge; the blade of a petal or the upper spreading part of a gamopetalous corolla.

Linear: Long and narrow, about uniform in width.

Lip: One of the two divisions of a two-lipped corolla or calyx.

Littoral: Growing under the influence of the sea.

Lobe: A more or less rounded division of an organ.

Lodicule: One of two or three small hyaline scales in the florets of grases inside the lemma and palea, subtending the stamens and pistil.

Lunate: Crescent-shaped.

Lyrate: (leaves) With the terminal lobe large and rounded.

Marcescent: Withering but not falling off.

Membranaceous or **membranous:** Like a membrane; thin pliable translucent.

-merous: A suffix meaning parts. A 4-merous flower has four each sepals petals stamens and carpels.

Monadelphous: Stamens united into one set by their filaments.

Moniliform: Like a string of beads.

Monoecious: Of one household. Having two types of flowers on the same plant. Staminate flowers in one inflorescence, pistillate in another, as in Firs, Oaks and Alders.

Mucronate: Ending abruptly in a short sharp but rather soft point.

Muricate: Rough with short hard elevations.

Naked: Without covering or appendages. Naked stem, one without leaves; naked flower, one without perianth.

Nerve: A simple prominent vein.

Node: A point on the stem from which a leaf or branch developes.

Nut: An indehiscent one-seeded fruit developed from a compound ovary.

Ob—: A prefix meaning reversed; in an opposite direction.

Oblanceolate: Inversely lanceolate.

Oblique: Unequal sided; slanted.

Oblong: Two or three times longer than broad, the sides more or less parallel.

Obovate: Inversely ovate.

Obsolete: Occuring as vestiges; scarcely developed.

Obtuse: Blunt or rounded at the tip.

Offset: A short lateral prostrate branch, rooting and eventually producing a separate plant; a short stolon.

Opposite: Occuring in pairs on opposite sides of stem.

Orbicular: Circular or roundish in form.

Ovary: The enlarged basal part of the pistil in which the ovules are developed.

Ovate: Egg-shaped in outline.

Ovule: The undeveloped seed in the ovary.

Palea: The smaller upper bract opposite the lemma, the two enclosing the floret in the grasses; chaff or chaffy bracts.

Palmate: Digitate. Leaflets lobes divisions or veins radiating from the apex of the petiole like the fingers of the hand.

Panicle: A compound flower cluster caused by extensive branching; a compound raceme, or loosely applied to any irregular compound inflorescence.

Papilionaceous: Literally butterfly-like; the characteristic corolla of the Pea family. An irregular corolla with an upper petal, the banner; two lateral petals, the wings; and two lower petals joined to form the keel.

Papillate or **Papillose:** Beset with papillae; having minute blunt protuberances.

Pappus: The modified calyx-limb borne on the achenes of the Composite family; feathery, bristle-like, scales or chaff.

Parietal: (placenta) Borne on the walls of the ovary; ovules attached to the walls not the axis.

Parted: (leaves) The blade cut nearly to the midrib or petiole.

Pectinate: Cut into closely set divisions resembling the teeth of a comb.

Pedate: Resembling a bird's foot; palmately divided, the two lateral divisions two-cleft.

Pedicel: The stalk of a flower in a flower cluster. Pediceled, having a pedicel.

Pedicellate: Having a small or short pedicel.

Peduncle: The stalk supporting a flower cluster or a single flower when solitary.

Pellucid: Clear, transparent.

Peltate: Shield- shaped; round, the petiole attached on the under side at the middle instead of at the margin.

Pendulous: Hanging down, drooping, pendent.

Perfect: A flower having both stamens and pistils.

Perfoliate: Leaves or stipules with clasping bases that are united beyond and appear to be pierced by the stem.

Perianth: The floral envelopes, calyx and corolla taken together; or either of them if one is lacking.

Perigynium: A sac-like bract enclosing the carpel in the genus *Carex*.

Perigynous: Around the ovary, inserted on the calyx.

Persistent: Remaining attached or falling away very tardily.

Petal: One of the parts of the corolla usually colored. Petaloid, petal-like.

Petiole: The stalk of a leaf.

Petiolule: The stalk of a leaflet.

Phyllopodic: Having the leaves at the base of the stem.

Pilose: With soft slender spreading hairs.

Pinna: A leaflet of a pinnate leaf.

Pinnate: With the leaflets arranged along each side of the rachis (midrib).

Pinnatifid: Pinnately cleft or parted.

Pinnule: A segment of a pinna.

Pistil: The seed producing organ of a flower, composed of a single carpel or of two or more united.

Pistillate: Having pistils but no stamens.

Placenta: That part of the ovary which bears the ovules.

Planc: Flat and even.

Plicate: In folds.

Plumose: Feather-like; finely branched.

Pod: A general term for any dry dehiscent fruit; a legume or follicle.

Pollen: The microspores, usually a fine yellow dust developed within the anther; essential to fertiliza-tion.

Polygamous: Having both perfect and imperfect flowers on the same plant.

Polypetalous: Having the petals distinct; opposite of gamopetalous.

Pome: A fleshy apple-like fruit developed from a compound ovary.

Posterior: The side behind; in an axillary flower the side next to the axis; superior.

Prickle: A rigid hard outgrowth of the epidermis, as the rose "thorn."

Procumbent: Lying on the ground; prostrate.

Proliferating: Producing supplementary shoots from near the summit or from an inflorescence; rapid production of new growth.

Proximal: Near the point of attachment.

Pruinose: Covered with a white bloom of fine waxy particles; densely glaucous.

Punctate: Dotted with point-like depressions.

Pungent: Tipped with a hard prickly point.

Pustulate: Having a blister-like elevation.

Raceme: A simple flower cluster in which the pedicels along the peduncle are about of equal length, the lowest flowers blooming first.

Rachilla: In grasses the axis of a spikelet bearing the florets.

Rachis: The axis of a compound leaf; the axis of a spike, raceme, or branch of a panicle; in grasses the branches of an inflorescence on which the spikelets are borne.

Radiate: Spreading from a common center; bearing rays.

Ray: A primary branch of a compound umbel; the ligule of a ray flower.

Receptacle: The axis or support of the parts of a flower or the flowers of the head in Compositae.

Recurved: Curved back.

Reflexed: Bent abruptly backward.

Regular: Having the parts in a circle uniform in size and shape.

Remote: More or les distant from each other.

Reniform: Kidney-shaped.

Repand: With margin slightly wavy.

Reticulate: With veins forming a network.

Retrorse: Turned back or downward.

Retuse: With a broad shallow notch at apex.

Revolute: Rolled backward from the margin or apex upon the lower surface.

Rhizome: Rootstock; an underground stem producing shoots and roots.

Rib: Primary vein of a leaf.

Rootstock: See rhizome.

Rostrate: Beaked or spurred.

Rotate: Wheel-shaped.

Rugose: Having wrinkles.

Runcinate: Sharply incised, the teeth turned toward the base.

Runner: A long slender basal branch rooting at the tip and more or less at the nodes forming new plants.

Saccate: Sac-like.

Sagittate: Shaped like an arrowhead.

Salient: Projecting outward as the segments of a leaf; prominent.

Salverform: (corolla) Having the limb spreading at right angles to the long slender tube.

Samara: An indehiscent dry one-seeded winged fruit, as in Maples and Ashes.

Saprophyte: Plants living upon decaying organic matter and without chlorophyll.

Scabrous: Rough to the touch.

Scale: A small thin body usually a modified leaf.

Scape: A leafless stem arising from the ground bearing flowers.

Scarious: Thin dry not green.

Scorpoid: Coiled at the tip.

Scurfy: Covered with small bran-like scales.

Secund: Inserted on one side of the stem; one-sided.

Seed: The fertilized matured ovule containing the embryo plant.

Sepal: One of the outer set of floral leaves forming the calyx.

Septate: With one or more septa or partitions.

Sapticidal: A capsule splitting between the partitions of the cells.

Septum: A partition in an ovary or fruit.

Sericeous: Silky; with appressed fine soft straight hairs.

Serrate: Saw-toothed; with teeth turned forward or upward. Serrulate, the diminutive.

Sessile: Without a stem or stalk.

Seta: A bristle or thick stiff hair.

Setaceous: Bristle-like.

Setose: Bristly; beset with bristles.

Sheath: A modified petiole or the basal part of the leaf when it encloses or sheathes a part of the stem just above the node, as in grasses.

Shrub: A low branching woody perennial usually without a distinct trunk; a bush.

Silicle: A short silique little longer than wide.

Silique: Pod of the Cruciferae several times longer than wide, two-celled the valves splitting from the bottom.

Simple: Unbranched, undivided, not compound.

Sinistrorse: Twining in a spiral from right to left; opposed to dextrorse.

Sinuate: With a deep wavy margin.

Sinus: The depression between two adjoining lobes, as of a leaf.

Smooth: Surface even, without roughness.

Sordid: Of a dull or dirty white color.

Spadix: A floral spike with a fleshy axis.

Spathe: A sheathing bract enclosing a flower cluster, such as a spadix.

Spatulate: Shaped like a spatula; broad and rounded at apex, narrowed below to a slender base.

Spicate: Spike-like.

Spike: An elongated flower cluster in which the flowers are sessile and more or less congested along the common peduncle.

Spikelet: A secondary spike; the flower cluster of grasses.

Spine: A sharp pointed hard woody deep-seated process, a modified branch or leaf.

Spur: A slender sac-like extension of the base of a corolla or calyx.

Squama: A scale.

Squamose: Squamous; scaly; provided with squamae.

Squamulose: Minutely squamose.

Squarrose: Wide-spreading or curved outward, as the tips of bracts.

Stamen: A male floral organ bearing pollen grains.

Staminate: Bearing stamens only.

Staminodium: A sterile stamen, usually the filament only.

Standard: See banner.

Stellate: Star-shaped; with slender divisions radiating from a common center, as stellate hairs.

Sterile: Barren; not capable of reproduction.

Stigma: The receptive part of the style at the tip of the pistil, commonly covered with a sticky substance.

Stipe: The stalk-like base of an ovary or fruit.

Stipitate: Having a stipe.

Stipules: A pair of appendages, usually leaf-like, borne at the base of the petiole.

Stipulate: Having stipules.

Stolon: A slender basal branch or shoot developing a bud and root at the tip or at both node and tip.

Stoloniferous: Producing stolons.

Stomata: Minute pores on leaves and stem.

Striate: Marked with slender lines groves or ridges.

Strict: Close narrow erect; not spreading.

Strigose: With appressed rigid straight hairs.

Strobile or **strobilus:** A cone, q.v.

Style: The slender stalk-like part of the pistil bearing the stigma.

Stylopodium: The dilated disk-like exapnsion at the base of the style in Umbelliferae.

Sub—: A prefix meaning nearly or below.

Subcordate: Nearly cordate.

Submerged or **submersed:** Growing under water.

Subtend: To be situated closely beneath; to enclose.

Subulate: Awl-shaped; narrow, tapering from base to apex.

Succulent: Having juicy tissues.

Sucker: A branch or shoot from an underground stem tending to become a separate plant.

Sulcate: Grooved or furrowed.

Superior: (ovary) Above the other organs; when the stamens calyx and corolla are free from and attached below the ovary.

Symmetrical: (flower) with the same number of parts in each circle.

Sympetalous: See gamopetalous.

Synsepalous: See gamosepalous.

Taproot: A single main root growing vertically downward with small lateral roots.

Terete: Round in cross section; cylindric.

Ternate: Occuring or divided into 3s.

Tetradynamous: Having four long and two short stamens, as in Cruciferae.

Thorn: A sharp-pointed hard woody process, homologous with a stem; a medified branch produced from a bud.

Throat: (calyx or corolla) The upper expanded part of the tube.

Thyrse: A contracted or dense panicle, as certain species of *Penstemon* and the cultivated Lilac.

Tomentose: Having soft or woolly hairs.

Torulose: cylindrical, bulging at intervals, as certain seed pods.

Tri—: A prefix meaning three or thrice.

Trifid: Three cleft; tridentate.

Trifoliate: Having three leaflets.

Tripinnate: Thrice pinnate.

Triternate: Thrice ternate.

Truncate: Cut off squarely at the end.

Tuber: A thickened fleshy underground stem, as the potato.

Tufted: Closely clustered; many growing close together in a tuft.

Umbel: A flat-topped inflorescence, the pedicels all of equal length and originating from the same point.

Umbellet: A secondary umbel of a compound umbel.

Umbo: A knob topping one of the scales of a pine cone.

Undulate: Repand; with slightly wavy margins.

Unguiculate: Petals having a claw.

Urceolate: (calyx or corolla) **Urn-shaped:** globular and contracted at the mouth.

Utricle: A one-seeded indehiscent dry fruit with a thin membranous covering, the pericarp, as the fruit of the Chenopodiaceae.

Valvate: Opening by valves; meeting together by the edges without overlapping.

Var.: Variety. A division of a species.

Vein: A fibrovascular bundle for support and conduction.

Ventral: The side facing the axis; upper; inner; anterior. The opposite of dorsal.

Versatile: Turning freely on its support, said of anthers attached by their middle to the filament.

Verticil: Whorl; three or more leaves or other organs in a circle about a stem or other axis.

Verticillate: Arranged in a verticil.

Villous: With long shaggy hairs.

Virgate: Wand- or rod-like; with long straight stiff branches.

Viscid: Sticky.

Whorl: Same as verticil.

Wing: Any thin wing-like expansion or part; the lateral petals in a papillionaceous flower.

Wort: A plant or herb.

INDEX TO COMMON AND SCIENTIFIC NAMES